TEACH YOURSELF BOOKS

ELECTRICITY
IN THE HOUSE

**Some other
Teach Yourself Books**

TEACH YOURSELF BOOKS
ELECTRICITY
IN THE HOUSE

J. E. MACFARLANE
B.Sc.(Eng.), M.I.E.E., A.M.I.Mech.E.

TEACH YOURSELF BOOKS
ST. PAUL'S HOUSE   WARWICK LANE
LONDON EC4

First Printed   1945
This Impression   1970

Revised edition
Copyright © 1958
The English Universities Press Ltd

SBN 340 05570 7
PRINTED IN GREAT BRITAIN FOR
THE ENGLISH UNIVERSITIES PRESS LTD
BY LOWE AND BRYDONE (PRINTERS) LTD
LONDON

FOREWORD

THE AIM of the building section of the Teach Yourself Series is to assist those who are desirous of acquiring information concerning building methods and practice.

It is not intended that these books will take the place of textbooks or recognised courses of study at Technical Colleges, but they should appeal to all students of building because each volume has been written by a specialist in his own particular subject.

The series covers almost every branch of the building crafts and allied professional practice.

In placing before the public this comprehensive work on Building, no apology is necessary for continuing to describe and illustrate traditional methods of building construction, because it is of vital importance that the layman who desires to become acquainted with building technique should be instructed in the basic principles of building.

There is really very little difference between traditional methods of building and the form of construction which has been developed to meet the requirements of the immediate post-war era. As pre-fabrication and standardisation will be the main features in the construction of post-war buildings, these materials and methods have been described and illustrated within the framework of this series, but no attempt is made to theorise on their comparative values.

Electrical installation is an essential part of the service equipment of a modern house, and therefore it is necessary for the house-owner to become acquainted with the principles underlying correct installation.

In this volume the author has outlined in a concise and practical manner the fundamental principles of electrical installation, including wiring, accessories, and fittings. The diagrams throughout the book are presented in a clear and simple form particularly suited to the requirements of readers who desire to acquire knowledge concerning this very important section of building technique.

PREFACE

THIS volume in the Teach Yourself Building Series is intended for students of all ages who wish to gain some insight into the electrical apparatus and installation of a modern house, without having to refer to larger works of a more technical nature on electrical engineering practice.

It is hoped that the contents will prove useful and interesting to students of Building and Architecture and junior classes in Electrical Installation work, besides all those interested in housing during the period of rehabilitation which is now being considered.

The author wishes to express his thanks to numerous friends for their help and suggestions, and to Mr. H. H. Walter, A.M.I.E.E., for reading the MS., also the Institution of Electrical Engineers and the following manufacturing firms: Messrs. Aidas Electric Ltd., Bill Switchgear Ltd., British Thomson-Houston Co. Ltd., British Trane Co. Ltd., British Insulated & Callender's Cables Ltd., J. A. Crabtree & Co. Ltd., Dorman & Smith Ltd., General Electric Co. Ltd., English Electric Co. Ltd., Liverpool Electric Cable Co. Ltd., Nalder Bros. & Thompson Ltd., and Simplex Electric Co. Ltd.

LIVERPOOL   J. E. M.

CONTENTS

CONTENTS

LIST OF PLATES

LIST OF TABLES

ELECTRICITY AS A UTILITY AND LABOUR-SAVING AGENT

In this country we are fortunate in having a good supply of pure water and it is one of the public utilities we take for granted. At the present time plans are being considered for atomic power development, and the provision of large numbers of houses will be one of paramount importance.

Electricity is a public utility which must be considered in conjunction with plans for any building, whether it is the humblest cottage or a luxurious block of flats. Light, airy houses will be popular after the dingy black-out conditions of war-time, and every effort must be made to take full advantage of all amenities in the new construction.

Electricity is an essential portion of the modern house, and due thought must be given to its inclusion to give a harmonious whole and not as an item to be added as an afterthought. Much progress has been made in the last generation, but in the next decade the extension will be greater still. The supply of electrical energy is now a nationalised undertaking with twelve Area Boards and the Electricity Council which is an advisory body. The Government Department concerned is the Ministry of Fuel and Power, who operate the Electricity (Supply) Acts 1882 to 1926 together with later additions.

As a labour-saving agent electricity is clean, convenient, and controllable. It is essential that electrical installations should be installed by competent electricians and such important work should not be given to any odd handyman who can use a pair of pliers and a bit of flexible wire. The National Register of Electrical Installation Contractors* has been in operation for a number of years and possession

---

* Now the National Inspection Council for Electrical Installation Contracting.

of this registration certificate is a guarantee of efficient workmanship, as is membership of the Electrical Contractors Association.

Effects of an Electric Current

We are not concerned with what electricity actually is—though the electron theory is established on our present experience—but how it can be used in the service of man. Our concern is with the effects and how electricity can be employed in a useful and efficient manner. The inventive genius of man has devised many machines to enable him to carry out tasks beyond the capabilities of his own pair of hands, from the primitive wedge and roller used to build the Pyramids to the mighty turbines of 200,000 horse-power in a modern power-station. The effects of an electric current are worth knowing and are given in the following sections.

Heating Effect

When an electric current flows in a conductor, heat is produced. The electric fire is a common example, in which the element, made of a special sort of wire, is raised to a red heat. The electric lamp depends upon this effect, as the filament is so hot that it is incandescent and emits light. These are useful applications, but if a wire carries too great a current for its size, then dangerous overheating will result, with a consequent fire-risk, which must be guarded against.

Magnetic Effect

Everyone is familiar with the horse-shoe magnet, which will pick up iron nails, pen-nibs, and small pieces of steel. The magnetic compass (see Fig. 1) consists of a magnetised needle mounted on a pivot and points in the direction of the magnetic meridian. When a wire is carrying an electric current it is surrounded by a magnetic field and behaves in a similar way to a magnet. If the wire is wound up into a coil a very much stronger effect is produced, which can be made greater still by winding the wire on an iron rod. But this large magnetic effect is only present whilst the current is flowing. This property is employed to obtain a magnet when and as required and is called an " electro-magnet." Special hard steel can be given permanent magnetism by such a method: that is, they retain the magnetism evoked when the electric current in the coil is discontinued, whilst, on the other hand, soft iron loses practically all its magnetism when the current ceases. In the construction of electro-magnets, soft-iron cores in the form of solid rod, iron wire, or strips of thin iron sheet are employed. This magnetic

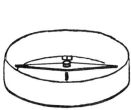

Fig. 1.—Magnetic Compass pointing North.

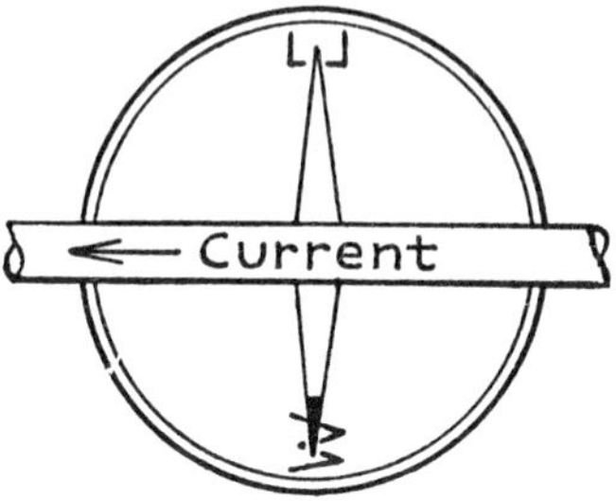

Fig. 2.—Current deflecting a Magnetic Compass.

effect is employed in electric bells, telephones, and indicating devices. If a wire carrying a steady electric current is placed over a magnetic compass needle, as in Fig. 2, then with the current flowing in one direction the needle will be deflected one way and on reversal of the current the direction of movement is reversed. This principle is employed in various types of instruments and meters used for measuring electric pressure, current, and power, besides its application to motors, generators, transformers, and other devices. The discovery by Michael Faraday of electro-magnetic induction, over a hundred years ago, laid the foundation of electrical power and machinery. If electric conductors adjacent to one another carry excessive currents, then, besides the dangerous heating effect, there is a magnetic force between them which tends to tear them from their supports, but this does not occur in domestic installations with relatively low currents.

Chemical Effect

If two wires from a flat flash-lamp battery are dipped into a glass containing water, to which a few drops of vinegar are added, bubbles of gas will be seen to form on the wires when they are brought sufficiently close together *without* touching. This shows that the water has been split up into its constituent elements, oxygen and hydrogen, which are evolved as gases.　If the same wires are stuck in a potato, about $\frac{1}{16}$ inch apart, then the wire connected to the positive terminal of the battery will show a green discoloration, due to the effect of the current on the chemical constituents of the potato.　Do *not* try this with the main supply or the results will be unpleasant.　This effect is usefully employed in the electro-deposition of metals and refining.　It is also evident as apparent corrosion when there is a leakage of electric current from a cable to adjacent metal-work.

Arc Effect

If two carbon rods connected to a suitable supply are momentarily touched together and then separated, an intense spark called an " arc " is formed.　With sufficient electric pressure across the space the current does not cease but persists in the form of an arc.　The temperature of the carbons is about 6300 degrees Fahrenheit and an intense white light is emitted mainly from the incandescent carbons. This effect is usefully employed for searchlights, photographic processes, electric furnaces, and electric arc-welding. A similar effect can occur with a break in an electric cable, when the arc may persist between the broken ends or to any nearby metal-work, again constituting a fire-risk.　Arcs also occur at switch-contacts, and when the current is interrupted in certain types of circuits in a careless manner at the wrong position instead of using the proper switch.

Physiological Effect

This is the " electric shock " to the organs of the body which is dangerous and may even be fatal. For this reason care should be exercised with electrical connections. Switches should be " off " or the fuses withdrawn when any alterations or repairs are being made to the wiring of a house. " Safety first " must be considered at all times with electrical apparatus. Perhaps we can consider as a useful application of this effect its use in the course of justice at Sing-Sing Prison !

Electrical Units

Before we are able to compare the sizes of different objects we must have some system of suitable units. A yard-stick is suitable for measuring a length of cloth, but it is of no use in weighing coal or finding the hours of sunlight on a certain day The scientific basic units are the centimetre for length, the gram for mass, and the second for time.* All the practical electrical units are related to these dimensions, but we are concerned only with their application and can be thankful to the scientists for providing a method of measurement.

Electricity is a form of energy, which may be defined as the ability to do work; so when energy is expended, work is done. Electrical energy is paid for in the electricity bill, even though the account may include some charges for other services, such as the hire of an electric cooker.

The legal unit for the sale of electrical energy is the kilowatt-hour (abbreviated to kWh.). As this unit was originally authorised by the Board of Trade, it is often called the " Board of Trade unit," or simply " unit."

Energy is the rate of doing work multiplied by time, and the rate of doing work is called power. In every-day speech a motor-van is more " powerful " for shifting a load than a horse and cart, thus the former does more work in a given time than the latter. If a labourer carries 20 lb. of

* The Metre, Kilogram, Second or M.K.S. system, is now used in electrical engineering.

sand 30 feet up a ladder, then 600 ft.-lb. of work has been done, whether he takes 2 minutes or 2 hours over it; but in the former case the rate of doing work is sixty times quicker than in the latter.

The electrical unit of power is the watt. It is used when referring to a 60-watt lamp, which is more powerful than a 25-watt lamp. The unit quantity of electricity is the coulomb, comparable with the gallon as a quantity of water; but we are only concerned with the rate of electrical flow or current. This is the quantity of electricity flowing in a circuit in a unit of time, the second. This is called the ampere, often abbreviated to amp., or A. In a water-main we are not concerned with how many gallons it will hold, but the delivery in gallons per minute; so in just the same way we are interested only in the flow of current in an electric cable or how much current we must make flow in an electric fire to make it red-hot. A level water-main full of water would not deliver any water to the domestic kitchen tap without the pressure behind the water, thus pressure effects the rate of flow. This is obtained either by the height of a reservoir above the main or the pumps at the waterworks. In the electricity main or cable it is the pressure generated at the power-station which causes the electric current to circulate around the supply system. This pressure is measured in volts and is present all the time, whether we have the electricity turned on, by means of a switch, or not. Thus the electrical power available depends upon both the pressure and intensity of flow. Hence electrical power in watts is the product of the pressure in volts and the current in amperes.

The difference in pressure, or potential difference (abbreviated to p.d.), across the ends of a circuit causes a current to flow, if the circuit is complete. But what settles the magnitude of the current? If we have a new clean water-main, very little pressure will send the water along it, as the friction between the moving water and the walls of the pipe is very low. Suppose the main is half-full of sand and gravel, then a very much higher pressure will be needed to deliver the same quantity of water in a given time; also a smaller clean pipe would require a greater pressure and velocity to deliver water at the same rate. The total resistance to flow will depend upon the length of the pipe, its internal cross-sectional area, and its material wetted surface. In a similar manner the conductor material, such as copper, of an electrical circuit is like the bore of a water-main and offers a resistance to the rate at which electricity is supplied. So it can be said that the rate of quantity of electricity increases with the pressure and decreases with the resistance. This statement is the basis of Ohm's Law, which can be given as: Current is proportional to the voltage and inversely proportional to the resistance.

The unit of resistance is the ohm. A p.d. of 1 volt applied to a resistance of 1 ohm will cause a current of 1 ampere; alternatively voltage divided by ohms gives amperes. In letters, I stands for current, V for pressure, and R for resistance, i.e. $I = \dfrac{V}{R}$ or $V = I \times R$ or $R = \dfrac{V}{I}$. If any two of these quantities are known, then the third one can be found. Power, in watts, is the product of voltage and current, therefore $V \times I = P$.

This product is true power in Direct-current Circuits, but has to be multiplied by another quantity called " power-factor " to give true power in Alternating-current Circuits. But in household installations this refinement is generally unnecessary. The watt is too small a unit for many installations, so kilowatts are employed, which are thousands of watts, and 1 kilowatt for 1 hour is 1 unit of energy.

Example 1. An electric fire, having a resistance of 40 ohms, is connected to a 200-volt circuit. What current will it take and what will be the power in kilowatts ? If the cost of power is 1d. per unit, how much does it cost to use this fire for 3 hours ?

Current in amp. $= \dfrac{\text{volts}}{\text{ohms}} = \dfrac{200}{40} = 5$ amp.

Power in watts = volts × amp. = 200 × 5 = 1000 watts.

Power in kilowatts = watts ÷ 1000 = $\dfrac{1000}{1000}$ = 1 kW.

Energy = power × time = 1 kW. × 3 hr. = 3 kWh.

But 1 kWh. is one unit costing 1d.,

$$\therefore \text{cost} = 3 \times 1d. = 3d.$$

The mechanical unit of power is the horse-power which is equivalent to 746 watts and is used when machines are driven by electric motors.

FIG. 3.—Voltmeter, Portable Type.

(*Nalder Bros. & Thompson Ltd.*)

Measuring Instruments

The pressure is measured by a voltmeter, illustrated in Fig. 3, which shows a portable type of instrument and is *connected across* the mains or the apparatus concerned. This is like a pressure-gauge on a boiler which does not measure the steam consumption; in a similar way the voltage is not a measure of the current used.

The current is measured by an amperemeter, usually

FIG. 4.—Ammeter, Wall-mounting Type arranged for Conduit.
(*Nalder Bros. & Thompson Ltd.*)

called an ammeter, illustrated in Fig. 4, which is of the wall-mounting type arranged for conduit and is *connected in* the circuit, like a gas-meter in the gas-main.

The correct methods of connecting a voltmeter and an ammeter are shown in Fig. 5.

It is possible to connect the voltmeter across the supply mains, as it has a high resistance and so will not take a lot of current.

Example 2. A voltmeter which will read up to 250 volts has a resistance of 10,000 ohms. What current will it take when connected across a 200-volt supply ?

Current in amp. $= \dfrac{\text{volts}}{\text{ohms}} = \dfrac{200}{10,000} = \dfrac{1}{50}$ or 0·02 amp.

The ammeter, on the other hand, must *never* be connected across the supply, whether it is from the mains or a battery, as it will take a very large current, due to its low resistance, and suffer internal damage.

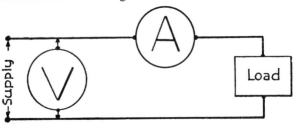

FIG. 5.—Method of connecting a Voltmeter and Ammeter.

Example 3. An ammeter to read up to 20 amp. has a resistance of $\frac{1}{100}$ ohm. What current will it take if accidentally connected across (*a*) a 12-volt car-battery; (*b*) the 230-volt mains ?

(*a*) Current $= \dfrac{12}{\frac{1}{100}} = 12 \times 100 = 1200$ amp.

(*b*) Current $= \dfrac{230}{0·01} = 230 \times 100 = 23,000$ amp.

In such a case the fuses would cut off the supply, but the ammeter would also be burnt out.

Example 4. What voltage is required across the above ammeter to give the full deflection of 20 amps ?

By Ohm's Law, volts $=$ current $\times$ resistance
$$= 20 \times \tfrac{1}{100} = \tfrac{1}{5} \text{ or } 0·2 \text{ volt.}$$

Supply Meters

These meters are the property of the Supply Undertaking and are sealed on installation, so that they cannot be tampered with by unauthorised persons. They combine the action of a voltmeter and ammeter and depend for their action on the magnetic effect, though on some direct-current systems an electrolytic type is employed which utilises the chemical effect of a current. Instead of a pointer as in an indicating instrument, the moving element rotates and drives a train of wheels which records the number of units consumed on a number of small dials.

How to read an Electricity Meter

A meter is easy to read and gives a check on consumption of electricity. On the smaller sizes there are four black

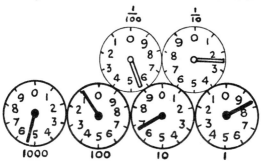

FIG. 6 (a).—Electricity Meter (10 amp.).

dials which register thousands, hundreds, tens, and single units. The hands of adjacent dials revolve in opposite directions. The red dials registering in tenths and hundredths of a unit may be disregarded as they are provided for testing purposes.

To read the meter, start at the right-hand dial of single units. When the hand is between two figures, write down the *lower* figure; if between 0 and 9, always write down 9. Repeat the process with the other dials, writing down the figures in the order right to left. If the hand is *on* a figure (say 6), write down 5, not 6, unless the hand on the previous right-hand dial is between 0 and 1. On larger meters there are five black dials going up to ten-thousands.

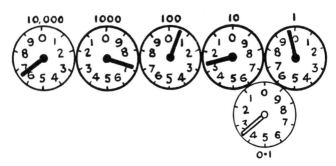

FIG. 6 (*b*).—Electricity Meter (50 amp.).

Example 5. In Fig. 6 (*a*) is shown the dial arrangement of a 10-amp. meter; the reading is 5068 units. Fig. 6 (*b*) shows a 50-amp. meter; the reading is 67,029 units. Now try these simple readings from Figs. 7 (*a*) and 7 (*b*). What do these dials read? The answers are given at the end of the chapter, but don't look at them until you have tried your skill.

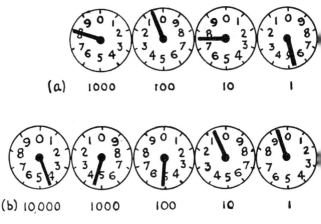

FIG. 7.—Electricity Meters to read.

Charges for Electricity

There are many scales of charges in different parts of the country and some perplexity is caused by the variety of methods employed. It is realised in the industry that rationalisation is desirable, and some progress has been made by the Area Boards.

Unfortunately, electricity cannot be generated at a steady rate and stored during the periods of low demand, like gas. Except for the relatively small amount that can be stored in " secondary cells " similar to the " accumulator " used on a D.C. radio-set, the power-stations have to be able to supply whatever amount is called for " on demand." This means that the generating plant installed must be large enough to supply the " peak " load, and not just the average load on the system. The advent of the Grid has helped to level out these peaks by the interconnection of stations, but they still exist. A week-day and Sunday load are shown in Fig. 8 for a large power-station, where these peaks are evident despite the levelling effort obtained by interconnection.

The capital charges on the plant together with the other standing charges must be met, besides the running costs of generation, which vary with the load. Two methods of framing tariffs are common:

(1) *Flat-rate Charges.* The price per unit is unchanged up to a certain minimum number of units per quarter, when a reduced price comes into effect. Meter rent is often an additional small item.

(2) *Two-part Tariff.* This consists of a fixed charge and a smaller price per unit than above. The fixed charge is arrived at in a variety of ways and may depend upon the floor-area of the premises, rating valuation, or power of lamps installed. This amount is justified by the standing charges referred to earlier. The flat rate is more usual for small flats or houses where electricity is used only for lighting. With additional heating and cooking load the two-part tariff is generally more economical for the house-

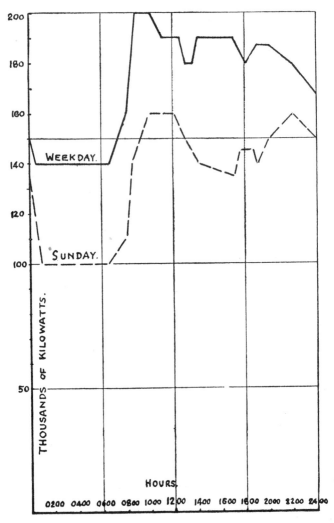

FIG. 8.—Load Diagram of a Large Power-station.

holder, besides ensuring a constant contribution to the fixed charges of the Supply Authority.

Example 6. A small householder has the choice of paying for electrical energy *either* (*a*) at a flat rate of 4d. per unit and 2s. 6d. a quarter meter rent; or (*b*) at a fixed charge of £2 per quarter plus $1\frac{1}{2}$d. per unit for all purposes. Which would be the cheaper tariff if the average quarterly consumption is (i) 150 units, (ii) 300 units? At what number of units per quarter would it be worth while changing from one scale to the other?

150 units per quarter

(i) Scale (*a*): 30d. meter rent + (150 × 4d.) = 630d. = £2 12s. 6d.

Scale (*b*): 480d. fixed charge + (150 × $1\frac{1}{2}$d.) = 705d. = £2 18s. 9d.

300 units per quarter

(ii) Scale (*a*): 30d. meter rent + (300 × 4d.) = 1230d. = £5 2s. 6d.

Scale (*b*): 480d. fixed charge + (300 × $1\frac{1}{2}$d.) = 930d. = £3 17s. 6d.

Scale (*a*) is the cheaper for 150 units, whilst Scale (*b*) is the cheaper for 300 units per quarter.

The answer to the latter part of the question is most easily illustrated by a graph. A graph is a mathematical picture showing how variable quantities are related. Two axes are drawn on squared paper like two sides of a square and marked off to scale in the units of the related quantities. The above figures can be used rearranged in the tables below as illustrated in the graph given in Fig. 9.

Scale (*a*)	Units per quarter .	0	150	300
	Total cost (pence) .	30	630	1230

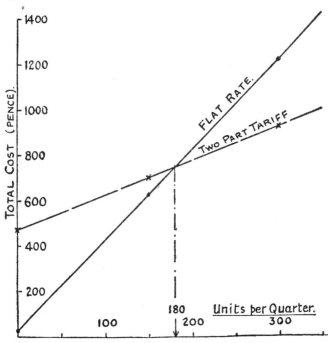

FIG. 9.—Graphical Comparison of Electricity Charges.

The " points " shown on the graph are joined by a straight line and labelled " Flat rate."

Scale (b)	Units per quarter .	0	150	300
	Total cost (pence) .	480	705	930

The " crosses " shown on the graph are joined by a straight line and labelled " Two-part tariff."

At least three sets of points should be taken to straddle the estimated consumption of the premises concerned. Where these two graphs cross one another shows the average number of units per quarter at which it is in the consumer's interest to change from the flat rate to the two-part tariff or vice versa.   This can be solved by a simple calcula-

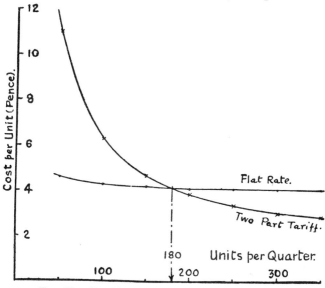

Fig. 10.—Graphical Comparison of Cost per Unit.

tion, as at the intersection the total charges are equal.   If x be the number of units, then:

$$30 + 4x = 480 + 1\tfrac{1}{2}x$$
$$\therefore 2\tfrac{1}{2}x = 450$$
$$x = 180 \text{ units, as obtained from the graph.}$$

As a matter of interest two other graphs are plotted in Fig. 10, showing the cost per unit against the number of units per quarter, and these two curves also intersect at 180 units per quarter.   These graphs bring out the advantage of the two-part tariff as the electrical load increases with the use of more domestic appliances.

Answer to Fig. 7 (a), 8075 units; Fig. 7 (b), 44,509 units.

CONDUCTORS AND INSULATORS

In two other public utilities, gas and water, the supply is distributed by the main pipes. To transmit electrical energy to the consumer, cables of various types and sizes are employed which consist of central conductors rather like the bore of a water-main, and the surrounding insulation which can be likened to the wall of the pipe (see Fig. 11). Any material which allows an easy passage to electricity is called a conductor. All metals are conductors of electricity, but some are better than others. Conductors are

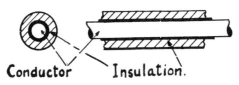

Conductor   **Insulation.**

Fig. 11.—Single-core Cable.

required to provide an easy path for the current and should not have a high resistance, or both drop of pressure and watts loss occur which will cause unwanted heating. Conductors are also required to control electric currents and pressures, such as the wire connecting a switch between a lamp and the supply. The most common metal for wires and cables is copper, which is specially refined to have high conductivity. Copper is easily tinned and soldered, also it is a ductile metal.

Aluminium is used to some extent for large sections, to carry heavy currents, but it cannot easily be soldered and special provisions have to be made for jointing.

Brass is employed for contacts and terminals, e.g. the brass plungers inside a lamp-holder.

Carbon is a non-metallic conductor and is used for sliding contacts on brass or copper, e.g. the carbon brushes which lead the current into the revolving armature of a motor. The lead of a pencil is a conductor, and it is possible to get a shock up a lead pencil if it is poked into an electric socket.

Iron is a poorer conductor than copper, due to its higher resistivity, and is not much employed as its magnetic properties may also cause extra losses.

Factors affecting the Resistance of a Conductor

The greater the length of a conductor the higher will be its resistance, and for a given length and material the resistance can be lessened by increasing the area of cross-section.   If

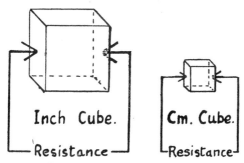

FIG. 12.—Illustrating Resistivity.

l is the length of a conductor in inches, a its cross-sectional area in square inches, and s its resistivity which depends upon the material of the conductor, then resistance is given by $R = \dfrac{s \times l}{a}$ ohms.

The "resistivity" of any material is the resistance between the opposite faces of a cube of the conductor which has an edge of unit length, which in the above case is 1 inch (see Fig. 12).   As copper has high conductivity it has low resistivity, and the resistance between the opposite faces of the cube is very small.   Any very small number less than one can be written as a decimal with a number of noughts in front of the first significant figure. For convenience, we work in " thousandths," denoted by milli, and millionths, denoted by micro, placed in front of the unit name. Thus 5 milli-amperes is 5 thousandths of an ampere, or $\frac{5}{1000}$ ampere, and 2 microhms is 2 millionths of an ohm, or $\frac{2}{1,000,000}$ ohm. For copper the resistivity, s, is $\frac{2}{3}$ microhm when using inch dimensions and cool copper, whilst in centimetre units it is $1\frac{2}{3}$ microhm. As metals get hotter their resistance increases, though the opposite effect occurs with carbon; but the above value for copper is easy for calculations and is sufficiently accurate for our purpose.

Example 7. A copper wire of 16 S.W.G. (Standard Wire Gauge) has a diameter of 0·064 inch, and a cross-sectional area of 0·0032 sq. inch. If its resistivity is $\frac{2}{3}$ microhm in inch units, what will be the resistance of 1000 yards ?

$$R = \frac{s \times l}{a} = \frac{2 \times (1000 \times 36)}{3 \times 1,000,000 \times 0·0032}$$
$$= 7·5 \text{ or } 7\frac{1}{2} \text{ ohms.}$$

Convert the length in yards to inches and see that the cross-sectional area is also in square inches, as the resistivity is given in inch units. Note that all the units must be of the same sort. This size of wire in a cable will carry 10 amperes, and a thousand yards will weigh about 37 lb. without the covering of insulation. As approximate figures for calculating weights, copper weighs $\frac{1}{3}$ lb. per cubic inch and iron $\frac{1}{4}$ lb. per cubic inch.

Example 8. If the above copper wire of 16 S.W.G. were cut in half and run side by side, what would now be the resistance of the two wires together ?

The length is now 500 yards, but the cross-sectional area is doubled to 0·0064 sq. inch, so by proportion:

$$R = 7·5 \times \frac{500}{1000} \times \frac{0·0032}{0·0064} = 1·875 \text{ or } 1\frac{7}{8} \text{ ohms.}$$

Insulators

Electricity will wander back to earth if not kept within bounds, and in so doing will be a nuisance, if not a definite danger. To keep it to its proper path in the conductor it is necessary to insulate the conductor. Insulators are necessary to insulate the conductor. Insulators are substances which are poor conductors of electricity and serve to prevent, as far as possible, an electric current straying from its conductor path. The pressure or voltage on an electric cable whilst sending the current along the conductor also tends to force a very small current through the wall of insulation around the conductor. If the insulation is insufficient or faulty, there will be a leakage current which will flow to earth and return to the power-station by any easy path, such as water-mains. Due to the contents of the soil, chemical action will occur causing corrosion, and this is more prevalent with direct-current than alternating-current systems. The insulation can be likened to the wall of a water-pipe which will only stand a certain hydraulic pressure before it begins to leak, and it may eventually burst. In a similar manner, if the pressure or voltage on an insulated wire is increased beyond a safe limit, the insulation will break down. Electric wires and cables are insulated for definite working pressures and should not be used for higher voltages. Thus a length of bell-wire is amply insulated for the 3-volts pressure obtained from two dry batteries, but it is most unsafe to use such wire on an " all-mains " wireless set working off 230 volts.

The resistivity of insulators is very high, and instead of writing a very large number with lots of noughts behind it we work in " thousands," denoted by kilo, and " millions," denoted by mega. Thus 2000 watts is called 2 kilowatts, and 600,000,000 ohms is called 600 megohms. The insulation resistance of cables is measured in megohms and decreases with increase of length, as there is more area of insulation, of the same thickness, for the leakage current to pass through.

Examples of insulators are india-rubber, both pure and vulcanised, gutta-percha, ebonite, mica, and slate. Some insulators are hygroscopic, i.e. absorb moisture, such as paper, cotton, silk, various built-up fibrous materials, and asbestos. As a general guide, good heat insulators are also electrical insulators, so that they tend to keep any heat in the conductor generated by the passage of the electric current. Continual overheating will cause the insulator to become hard and brittle and will perish rubber compounds, so cool running is essential for safety.

Simple Circuits

The two simple arrangements of conductors and connected apparatus in a circuit are called series and parallel.

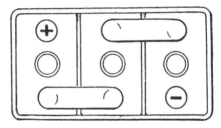

FIG. 13.—Car Battery, Three Cells in Series.

With two horses harnessed to a trap in tandem, they may be called in series, whilst two horses pulling a dray side by side are in parallel. The three cells of a 6-volt car-battery are connected in series as shown in Fig. 13. As each cell gives 2 volts, the total pressure adds up to 6 volts, and the current is common through each cell. If 8 amperes are taken for the lamps, then this amount of current is supplied by each cell. Two dry cells for an electric bell each give $1\frac{1}{2}$ volts. In Fig. 14 they are shown connected in series at (*a*), when the total voltage is 3. In (*b*) the similar terminals are connected together, then the pressure available is only that of one cell, namely $1\frac{1}{2}$ volts, but each cell will supply half the current, i.e. the total current in a parallel circuit is the sum of all the currents. In (c) the two negative wires are joined together, and the two positive terminals are shown going to the external circuit. This is incorrect, as the voltage of one cell is trying to send the current one way round the circuit

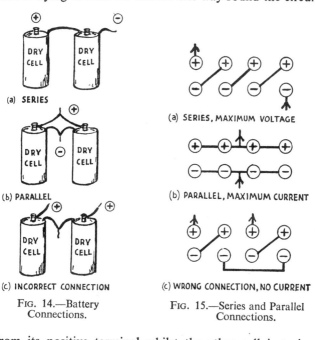

(a) SERIES

(b) PARALLEL

(c) INCORRECT CONNECTION

FIG. 14.—Battery Connections.

(a) SERIES, MAXIMUM VOLTAGE

(b) PARALLEL, MAXIMUM CURRENT

(c) WRONG CONNECTION, NO CURRENT

FIG. 15.—Series and Parallel Connections.

from its positive terminal whilst the other cell is trying to send the current round in the reverse direction. The net result is that the voltages are in opposition and no current will be supplied. With batteries there must be a positive and negative terminal. The series and parallel connections are shown diagrammatically for a 4-cell battery in Fig. 15 (a) and (b) respectively, whilst at (c) the connections are wrong.

Electrical energy is distributed on the parallel system,

in which the voltage is maintained constant, and all the separate currents add up to give the total load-current on the system. The same parallel method is employed inside the house, the various currents adding up to the total current supplied. The individual wiring, switch, and apparatus are connected in series, as the switch must open and close the circuit, and all these items will carry the same current.

Example 9. Suppose that in one room of a house the wife is ironing one evening ; the iron will take 2·2 amp. and a 60-watt lamp requires 0·26 amp. In another room the husband is listening to the radio whilst reading the paper, in front of an electric fire with one bar switched on. The radio will take 0·22 amp., a 100-watt lamp 0·44 amp., and the 1-kilowatt fire 4·4 amp., so the total current supplied to the premises is :

$$(2·2 + 0·26) + (0·22 + 0·44 + 4·4) = 6·92 \text{ amp.,}$$

say 7 amperes, in round figures.

The size of wire for each piece of apparatus must be large enough to carry the current and also be properly insulated to withstand the common pressure of 230 volts. The switches are in series with the individual apparatus they control, as shown in Fig. 16. From this it will be seen that each piece of apparatus has a common voltage of 230 and that the various streams of current combine to give a total of 7 amperes through the electricity meter. Note the switch on the electric fire for the second element ; the switch plug will disconnect the fire completely. The radio set will also have its own switch, but the pressure is on the connecting lead as long as the switch of its switch plug is closed.

Fuses and Cut-outs

The heating effect of an electric current may become dangerous, but this effect can be made use of to disconnect a circuit in which the current is excessive. Fuses are provided to protect both the wiring and connected apparatus as well

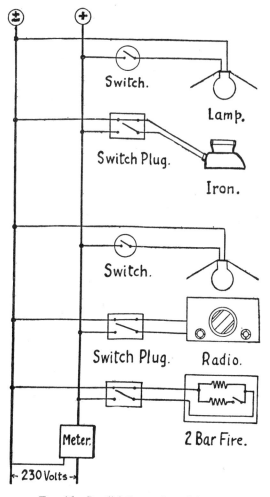

FIG. 16.—Parallel Connection of Apparatus.

as the adjacent structure of the building. Fuses are sometimes called " cut-outs," as they cut out the defective sections. This term is often given to the complete assembly of a case containing the fuses and contacts, but may be applied to an automatic switch which disconnects the section when an overload occurs. Such miniature circuit-breakers are employed in large houses, but fuses are much more common.

Fuses consist of short lengths of a suitable wire which will safely carry the normal current of the circuit, but with any sustained overload the wire melts. A very large current will blow the fuse immediately, whilst a lesser current may take several minutes to melt the wire. The correct size of wire must always be employed and *not* any odd bit of wire that is handy at the time.

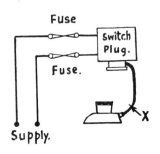

Fig. 17.—Effect of Short-circuit.

For simplicity no fuses were included in Fig. 16, but the various lighting and heating circuits would be divided up and suitably protected by fuses. The electric iron will be supplied by a flexible lead from the switch plug and two fuses are inserted between the connecting wires and the supply terminals as shown in Fig. 17. If everything is in order, the current will not cause any heating of the fuses and current will be supplied to the iron. Now supposing the two wires of the flexible lead are worn and so much of the insulation is rubbed off that the two bare wires can come in contact at the point X. This would cause a " short-circuit " and the current would take a short or easy path of very much lower resistance at the fault instead of going through the heater element of the iron. The current would surge up to a very large value and one or both of the fuses would melt. The current would be automatically cut off, before any damage was done to the rest of the circuit, as it could not get across the gap left by the melted fuses.

It is essential that the correct fuses should blow when anything is wrong, but they should not fuse unnecessarily. For this reason the size of fuses are graded to suit the various circuits, such as 5 amp. for the lighting circuit and 10 amp. for circuits carrying heavier loads.   The main fuses should not melt and cut off the whole supply to a house when a fault occurs on a sub-circuit ; this points to a bad installation.

Need for Switches in Live Side

The incoming supply to a house consists of the live or line wire and the neutral wire.   Switches are used for making and breaking an electrical contact, thus closing or opening an electric circuit.

The former paragraph showed why fuses were used. Figs. 18 and 19 show alternative connections of a lamp and

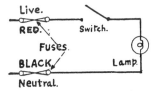
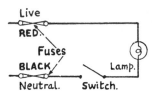

Fig. 18.—Switch in Live   Fig. 19.—Switch in Neutral
         Wire.   Wire.

switch.   In each case the switch will perform its function, but Fig. 18 is the *correct method* and Fig. 19 is *wrong*.   The invariable rule must be for all switches to be in the *live* wire, which is run with a red wire.   The reason is that the neutral (black wire) is connected to earth at the power-station, whilst the live wire (red wire) is connected to the supply pressure, which may be as high as 250 volts above earth potential.   Thus in Fig. 18 the supply pressure *above* earth is disconnected from the lamp when the switch is open and it is safe. With the switch as shown in Fig. 19 the lamp is still connected to the full pressure, which is dangerous, despite the switch being open.

Earthed Neutral

The maximum allowable pressure for domestic consumers is 250 volts, and this is the voltage between any one line conductor * and the neutral. The zero datum of the neutral is fixed by an earthed neutral point maintained by the supply authority. On alternating-current systems the supply authority may declare a multiple-earthed neutral system, which means that the neutral conductor is permanently earthed at several points. This will affect the installation in a house, as all fuses must be single-pole, i.e. single-pole cut-out assemblies are employed and not double-pole boards with solid links. With permanently connected earthed neutrals at sub-stations, the local regulations may require the consumer's fuses to be entirely single-pole. This declaration and instruction must be issued by the supply undertaking and not be assumed by the installation contractor. Without definite instructions to the contrary, double-pole fuse-boards must be used for both main and sub-circuits.

Upper and Lower Voltages

The supply authority provide two voltages, one greater than the other, their ratio depending upon the type of supply. An earthed system of electric supply is one in which one or more points (usually the middle wire or neutral point) are deliberately connected to earth. Thus the pressure on either live wire above earth is limited as a safety precaution.

Direct Current and Alternating Current

A direct current is one which flows in one direction only, which is said to be from the positive (+) terminal or pole to the negative (—) terminal or pole.

---

* The line conductor is a phase conductor in 3-phase 4-wire A.C. systems and either outer in 3-wire D.C. systems.

These markings will be seen on accumulators and some direct-current instruments, which will only indicate when the positive wire is connected to the positive terminal and the negative wire to the negative terminal.

An alternating current does not flow constantly in one direction, but reverses in a periodic manner. Over one half of the cycle the direction is positive and during the next half-cycle it is negative. The number of complete alternations per second is called the frequency, denoted by " f " or " $\sim$." There is no right and wrong way of connecting the two wires to A.C. instruments, as with D.C. voltmeters and ammeters.

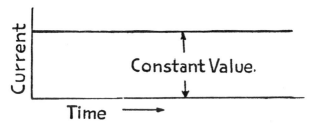

FIG. 20.—Direct Current.

Direct current can be represented by a horizontal straight line in the graph shown in Fig. 20, whilst alternating current is depicted by the wavy curve of Fig. 21. An alternating current of 1 ampere will do just as much work or light a lamp just as brilliantly as a direct current of 1 ampere. On a D.C. system the voltage has a steady value, whilst the alternating voltage varies in the manner indicated, but has just as much effective pressure to send the current around the circuit.

Domestic apparatus which is marked for a certain voltage will operate equally well on either type of current, unless it is specified as suitable for only one type. All appliances which depend upon the heating effect, such as radiators, irons, kettles, etc., can be used on either A.C. or D.C., at their rated voltages. Apparatus depending upon the magnetic effect may not work so well on A.C. as on D.C.,

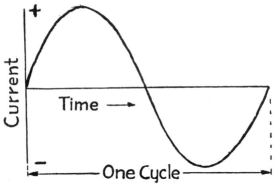

Fig. 21.—Alternating Current.

whilst in application of the chemical effect D.C. is required. One can get an equally painful electric shock from either A.C. or D.C., though the effects do vary.

Standard Voltages and Frequency

The term " consumer's voltage " denotes the voltage at the incoming terminals, declared by the supplier. This corresponds to the " declared pressure " in the Electric Lighting Acts. Domestic consumers are supplied on low voltages and the standards for new systems and installations are :

Direct-current Systems (Three-wire)

Consumer's Voltage (declared), 240 volts and 480 volts.

The former figure is that supplied for household use, and is the pressure between the live conductor, which may be either positive or negative, to the neutral conductor. The latter figure is the voltage between the positive and negative outers (both " live " conductors), which is used for driving motors and larger apparatus.

Alternating-current Systems (Three-phase)

Consumer's Voltage (declared).

Between neutral wire and each of the principal conductors, 240.

Between any two principal conductors, 415.

The former value is used for domestic installations, whilst the latter figure is used for larger power purposes. Large buildings and institutions may have the incoming supply at the higher voltage, but it is split up into the lower voltages for the separate circuits.

Frequency is now standardised in this country at 50 cycles per second. This means that there are 50 of the waves shown in Fig. 21 in every second, or the time of 1 cycle is 0·02 second. Apparatus of American origin is often only suitable for 60 cycles per second, which is commonly employed for lighting, though there are also 25-cycle systems. The frequency does not affect apparatus depending upon the heating effect, as will be evident from the preceding paragraph, but small motors, transformers, and any apparatus depending upon the magnetic effect of a current will only operate satisfactorily at the correct frequency for which they are designed. The above figures apply to a large number of supply authorities, but there may be systems existing in which the voltages vary from 100 to 250 and the frequencies from 25 to 100 cycles per second. Any undertaking will supply details of their standard voltages and conditions of supply. These should be obtained for reference purposes on new sites. The different types of tariffs are also included, together with any special local limitations on connected apparatus.

Effect of Incorrect Voltage

It is essential that apparatus of the correct voltage is installed, as otherwise, if the supply voltage is too high, damage may occur, whilst if it is too low the performance will be unsatisfactory. The voltage supplies the necessary impetus to send the current around the circuit to do the work required. Thus, if a 100-volt lamp is put in a lamp-holder connected to a 200-volt supply, there is twice the proper pressure applied and twice the current will flow through the lamp (whilst it lasts). Now, power (in watts) is proportional to the square of the current times the resistance, so in this case the power applied to the lamp is $(2)^2$, i.e. four times normal, and, of course, the lamp burns out. If, on the other hand, a 200-volt lamp is put on to a 100-volt supply, the current is only half of that required, so the power is $(\frac{1}{2})^2$, i.e. a quarter of normal, and the lamp is dull. Small differences of voltage have an effect on both the illumination and life, both of which will vary considerably with the differences in commercial voltages. Thus with a 1 per cent. increase of voltage on a metal-filament lamp, about $3\frac{1}{2}$ per cent. more light is obtained, but the useful life is shortened by some 12 per cent. With a 1 per cent. drop in voltage there is about $3\frac{1}{2}$ per cent. less light, but the useful life is lengthened by about 13 per cent.

Incoming Supply and Methods of Distribution

The provision of the supply is the responsibility of the supply authority who lay the service cable from the distributor running along the roadway. There may be a charge for opening up and connecting, and it is advisable to see that a large enough service cable is installed, though usually ample cable size is provided. The service cable is terminated at the supply company's fuses, which are sealed so that they cannot be interfered with by unauthorised persons and are on the incoming side of the electricity meters. The supply then goes to the main switch, which connects the installation to the meters, and thence through the consumer's fuses, which supply the distribution boards. The connection and maintenance of the meters is the responsibility of

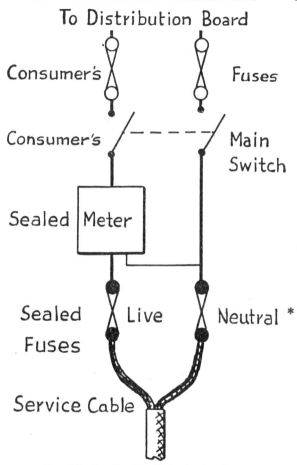

FIG. 22.—Leading in a Two-wire Supply.

the supply authority. This arrangement is shown in Fig. 22, which shows the leading in of a two-wire system. The service cables are connected to the distributors, which go back to the power-station or sub-station. A three-wire

* May be a solid link.

system of D.C. distribution is shown in Fig. 23. The live outers are marked positive (+) and negative (—) and the earthed neutral (±) is shown in between the two outers. Two-wire connections to separate domestic consumers are shown at A and B ; in each case one conductor brought into the house is connected to the live conductor and the other one to the earthed neutral. Connection C shows the connections to a large consumer, the wiring being divided

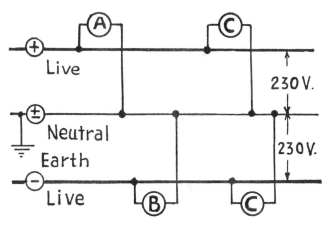

FIG. 23.—Three-wire D.C. Distribution.

into two entirely separate parts, the load being approximately balanced on each side.

Fig. 24 indicates diagrammatically a three-phase A.C. four-wire system, which is now most common. The three-pointed star represents the transformer in the sub-station, the mid-point of which is earthed and connected to the neutral conductor. The three-phase conductors form the live conductor and may be red, yellow, and blue or red, white, and blue. Inside the house RED is used for the live wire or phase-conductor and BLACK for the neutral, the two different colourings being used throughout. With a large building the three-phase, four-wire supply may be brought in and divided up as shown in Fig. 24. In this figure separate consumers having two wire connections are shown at A, B, and C, the different houses being balanced along the

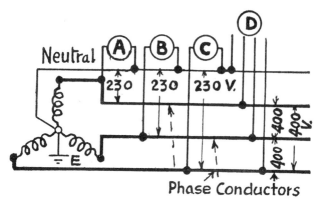

FIG. 24.—Three-phase A.C. Four-wire Distribution.

road. A large consumer might require to drive large motors ; then the connections would be as indicated at D, so that the line volts are 400 and the three voltages to neutral are each 230 volts. In the diagrams the joints are shown by a black dot, and where two wires cross over without any connection the black dot is absent.

The voltages as given in Fig. 24 are now being altered to 415 and 240 volts.

CHAPTER III

MAIN SWITCHES AND FUSES

The main fuses protect the whole installation and may be housed in a separate case or included with the main switch.

Modern practice is to use either iron-clad or moulded insulated main switches, which often include the main fuses. The main switch is of the double-pole type, so that the installation is completely disconnected from the supply when the switch is in the "off" position. With large A.C. installations triple-pole switches are used to connect the three-phase supply to the distribution board, where the supply is given to separate pairs of cables, made up by one connection from each phase and the common neutral link.

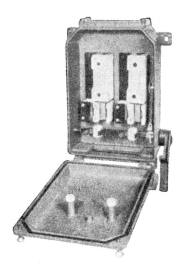

The main fuses are carried in porcelain carriers and the fuse-wire is completely protected from accidental contact. The cover of combined switch fuses is provided with a mechanical interlock which prevents the cover being opened unless the operating handle is in the "off" position. It is then safe to withdraw the fuses for replacement or to isolate the installation from the supply without the possibility of making or breaking the circuit on the fuse-carrier

FIG. 25.—Double-pole Switch Fuse.
(*General Electric Co. Ltd.*)

contacts and to prevent personal contact with live parts. The iron case must be earthed and a terminal is provided for this purpose.   The earthing wire should not be less than 7/·029 in. (·0045 sq. in.) tinned copper cable (7/·029 means 7 wires of ·029 in. diameter).   Standard sizes for main switches are 20, 30, 60, 100, and 200 amperes.   A double-pole main switch and fuses is shown in Fig. 25, whilst Fig. 26 shows a triple-pole switch fuse with neutral link.

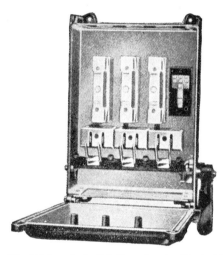

Fig. 26.—Triple-pole Switch Fuse showing Neutral Link.
(*Bill Switchgear Ltd.*)

Splitter Switches can be employed for small installations. These are combined main switch and fuses for the separate circuits.   Such an arrangement is cheap, but it is only allowed on small installations where the total current is about 30 amp., of which the lighting load may be 5 to 10 amp.   Splitter switches contain a main switch and two or three 15-amp. double-pole fuses in one case for 2-wire non-earthed installations.   Three sets of fuses are the maximum

E.H.—C

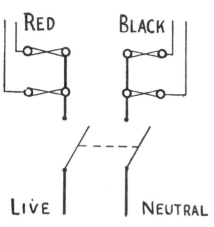

FIG. 27.—Two-way Splitter Switch.

permissible and there is no separate consumer's main fuse. A splitter switch with two ways is shown diagrammatically in Fig. 27 and illustrated in Fig. 28 (*a*), which is a three-way ironclad pattern. In 2-wire installations permanently and effectively earthed on one pole, single-pole switches are

FIG. 28 (*a*).—Three-way Switch Splitter (Ironclad).

(*Bill Switchgear Ltd.*)

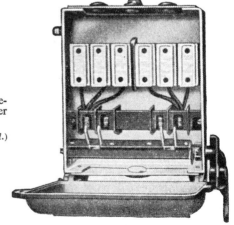

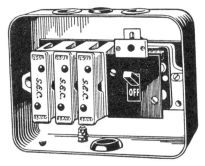

FIG. 28 (*b*).—Three-way Switch Fuse and Splitter.   Single-pole
and neutral.

(General Electric Co. Ltd.)

fitted in the phase or outer (non-earthed) conductor only,
as shown in Fig. 28 (*b*).

Main Circuits and Sub-circuits

The main switch and fuses look after the total current
demanded by the premises.   Composite units are now used
for domestic premises with 4, 5, 6 and 8 ways on A.C. circuits
up to 250 volts and single-pole fuses of 5, 15 or 30 amps.   The
total current can be compared to a river which gets its total
flow from a number of tributaries.   The sub-circuits are
the tributaries, and each one must be protected by its own
pair of fuses, so that if one section develops a fault it is cut
out, and so the trouble is isolated without the whole installation being disconnected.   The maximum number of
lamps on any one circuit is ten.   These are connected to one
pair of fuses.   With new installations, with the possibility
of extensions, only seven or eight lamps should be connected.
If there is any likelihood of additional domestic apparatus,
the number should be limited still further.

In Fig. 29 six lamps are shown connected to one pair of
fuses, in which L indicates a lamp and S the switch.   This is

a conventional diagram, and in practice " looping out "
is employed, as will be explained later on. It should be
noted that the switches S are connected to the RED WIRE on
the live or line side, whilst the lamps are connected to the
BLACK WIRE on the earthed neutral side.

With larger installations the various circuits are supplied
from a distribution board, the cables being suitably
arranged for convenience and economy. With large rooms

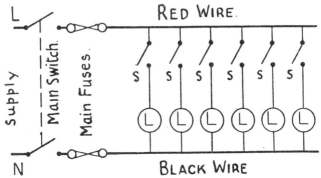

FIG. 29.—Circuit of Six Lamps.

two separate circuits may be used, so that if one branch
develops a fault there is enough lighting left for safety.
Switch plugs rated at 13 amp. are given separate circuits,
or arranged on a ring main.

If electrical energy is supplied through two meters, one
for lighting and the other for power, then entirely separate
circuits must be run with no possibility of interconnecting
the different types of load.

The main distribution board is supplied from the main
fuses by the bus-bars, which are cables large enough to carry
the total current and with some margin for future increase
of load.   Each circuit has two fuses,* one connected to each
bus-bar. This arrangement is shown in Fig. 30 for a
distribution board with five ways, each containing six lamps

* For 2-wire non-earthed installations.

and their associated switches. This is the most convenient arrangement for medium-sized houses when all the current passes through one meter. With an " all-in " tariff one distribution board is sufficient, though lighting and power circuits are separated because of the different current capacity.

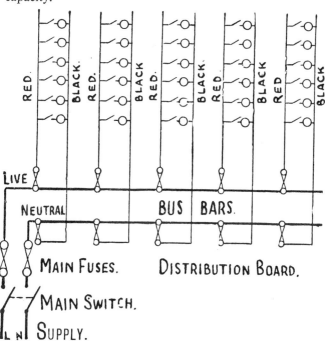

FIG. 30.—Five-circuit Distribution Board.

With separate scales of charges two separate distribution boards are required, and the wiring installation may be more expensive, due to longer cable runs. These arrangements are shown by single-line diagrams in Fig. 31. Water-heaters and cookers are also run on separate circuits, sometimes with a separate meter, main switch, and fuses.

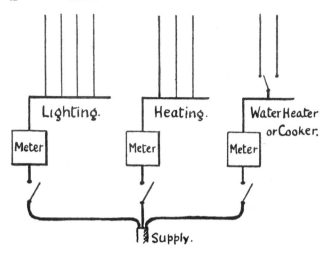

FIG. 31.—Single-line Diagram, Separate Metering.

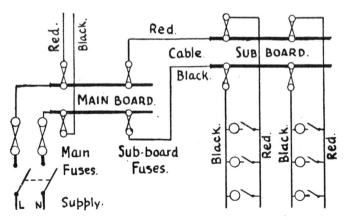

FIG. 32.—Sub-board fed from Pair of Fuses on Main Board.

Sub-distribution boards are necessary on large establishments with long cable runs, where the distance from the main distribution board would be too far for some final circuits due to excessive voltage drop.   A sub-board is fed from a pair of cables brought back to the main supply or main distribution board.   If this sub-board is connected

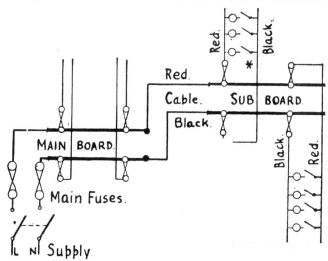

Fig. 33.—Sub-board directly connected to Main Board.   Bad practice.   * Note.—Switches incorrect in Black wire.

directly to the supply, its own switch fuse gives protection to the cables; but if it is connected to the main distribution board, the best practice is to do so with a pair of fuses as indicated in Fig. 32.   Fig. 33 shows another method which may save a few shillings on fuses but which is bad practice.   In the latter diagram the individual circuits from the sub-board are protected, but *not* the cables which add their load current to that already demanded by the main distribution board.   The main fuses will blow at twice the *total current* and will not give sufficient discrimination if a fault occurs on the cables to the sub-

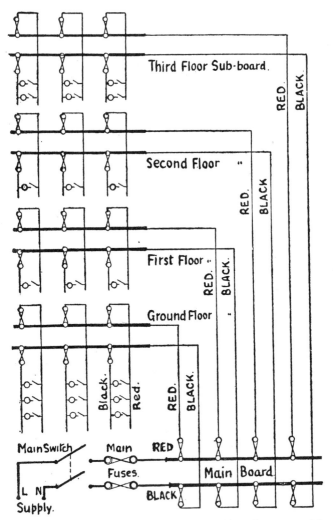

FIG. 34.—Main Distribution Board with Sub-boards connected by Fuses.

board.   Note the incorrect connection of three switches in
this diagram.

   For buildings with several floors of large extent the better
arrangement is shown in Fig. 34, in which each pair of rising
cables is connected to the main bus-bars by fuses.   Fig. 35

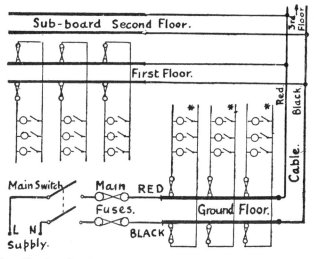

FIG. 35.—Looping in Sub-boards on Three Floors.   Rising cable
unprotected.   Bad practice.   * Note.—Switches incorrect in Black
wire.

is an example of bad practice : a single pair of rising cables
is shown.   The load on the cables tapers off as they go from
floor to floor, so the main fuses cannot give sufficient protection to the more remote portion of the cables.   The
ground-floor switches are shown incorrectly connected to
the black wire.

Installation Systems

   The various systems employed for installations depend
upon the class of work required, labour available, time to

complete, and the nature of the competition. During the present period of stringency rubber is in short supply, metals are controlled, and labour problems affect the work. With any system the avoidance of danger to life and safety of the structure should take precedence over other considerations.

In Table I below various wiring methods are listed in order of merit, but the comparisons must not be taken too literally.

TABLE I

Wiring Methods

System	Relative			Labour Required	Extensions and Renewals	Protection against		
	Cost	Life	Time to Install			Fire	Damp	Mechanical Damage
1 Conduit (metallic)	100	100	100	Skilled	Difficult	Very good	Good	Very good
2 Metal-sheathed (lead)	75	90	85	Skilled	Fairly easy	Fair	Good	Fair
3 Tough rubber-sheathed (or substitute)	60	90	50	Semi-skilled	Easy	Fair	Very good	Good
4 Cleat (temporary)	45	50	50	Semi-skilled	Easy	Poor	Poor	Poor

(1) Conduit System

This is the most satisfactory system, even if it is the most expensive. Steel tubes with screwed joints can be concealed in the walls during building. Even for surface work it is good, and by efficient installation it is possible to make the wiring practically waterproof and immune from mechanical damage. In normal times light- and heavy-gauge conduit is available, which may be solid-drawn seamless, welded with almost imperceptible joint or " close-joint," which is a longitudinal joint butting together. The heavy-gauge welded tube is used for high-class work, light-gauge welded conduit is most popular, whilst light-gauge " close-joint " is used for more competitive work. The latter should not be used when concealed, as it is not water-tight,

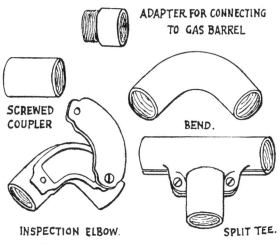

ADAPTER FOR CONNECTING TO GAS BARREL

SCREWED COUPLER

BEND.

INSPECTION ELBOW.

SPLIT TEE.

FIG. 36.—Some Screwed Conduit Fittings.

and must not be employed for over 250 volts. Conduit is generally finished in black enamel, inside and out, but for very damp situations galvanised finish is used. For some outside work gas barrel is fitted. It is thicker than conduit and needs adaptors to connect to conduit. Gas-barrel sizes are given in inside diameters, whilst conduit is specified by its outside diameter. Special fittings are necessary with conduit consisting of elbows, tees, bends, junction boxes, and inspection boxes ; these may be screwed or depend upon grip for continuity, as illustrated in Figs. 36 and 37.

The V.I.R. taped and braided wires are drawn into the conduit after it has been installed. The tube must not be packed tight with the wires ; there should always be room

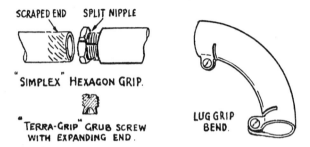

FIG. 37.—Grip Continuity Conduit Fittings.

(*Simplex Electric Co. Ltd.*)

to draw in one more conductor of the size already inside. It is possible to accommodate a greater number of wires in a short straight run than when there are a number of bends and junctions.

TABLE II

Wiring Capacity of Steel Conduit

Conductor of Cable		Heavy-gauge conduit				
Nominal cross-sectional area	Number and diameter (in.) of wires	$\frac{5}{8}$ in.	$\frac{3}{4}$ in.	1 in.	$1\frac{1}{4}$ in.	$1\frac{1}{2}$ in.
in.²		Maximum number of rubber-insulated and taped and braided or P.V.C.-insulated cables.				
0·0015	1/·044	5	7	13	20	—
0·002	3/·029	4	6	13	20	—
0·003	3/·036	3	5	10	16	—
0·0045	7/·029	3	4	9	13	—
0·007	7/·036	2	3	7	10	14
0·01	7/·044	—	2	5	8	11
0·0145	7/·052	—	—	4	7	9

In installations where there are many bends, an inspection bend should be fitted every third or fourth bend to facilitate drawing in; with long runs an inspection box is necessary.

The effect of bunching a number of wires together is to reduce the amount of current each wire can carry, as indicated in Table III. Thus four 3/·036-inch cables require ¾-inch conduit (from Table II) and the permissible current is 13 amp. (from Table III).

TABLE III

Current ratings for small house-wiring cables.

Number and diameter of wires (in.)	Two cables D.C. or single-phase A.C.	Four cables D.C. or single-phase A.C.	Three or four cables balanced 3-phase A.C.
1/·044	5	5	5
3/·029	10	10	10
3/·036	15	13	13
7/·029	20	15	15
7/·036	28	22	25

These current ratings are for single-core rubber-, P.V.C.-, or polythene-insulated cables, including tough-rubber, P.V.C.-, lead- or aluminium-sheathed cables run (i) bunched, and enclosed in one conduit, troughing or casing; (ii) bunched, in free air or an open trench.

Condensation in Conduit

In damp atmospheres where changes of temperature occur there is the possibility of moisture condensing inside the conduit. When the conduit is warm, the air inside it expands; and on cooling, air and moisture are drawn into the conduit. This " breathing " action can be minimised by making water-tight joints at the cable boxes and switches, with compound. The necessity for good continuity with either screw or grip fittings presupposes that all joints are

Fig. 38.—Special Earthing Conductor.
(British Insulated & Callender's Cables Ltd.)

clean and metal-to-metal. It has been found that red-lead and tow joints give almost as good electrical continuity as dry joints and have the advantage that they are water-tight. With long runs this method may not be desirable at every joint, but where the conduit is sunk and cement is floated on or much wet plaster is used this method is employed. The moisture tends to rust the inside of the conduit and is likely to be more troublesome on light-gauge than heavy-gauge conduit, especially if the enamelling is poor. With long vertical runs an open T-piece is sometimes fitted at the bottom to allow drainage and some ventilation, whilst horizontal runs are given a slight slope to the lowest point where a through box or T is fitted. The rusty patches and moisture also tend to affect the V.I.R. insulation of cables. For this reason conduit systems erected during building should be given some time to dry out before the cables are drawn in.

Continuity and Earthing

The conduit system must be continuous electrically and mechanically, and must be effectively connected to earth. The wire used for earthing must have a cross-sectional area of at least half that of the largest cable used and must not be smaller than 7/·029 inch (·0045 sq. inch). If this wire is bare it must be tinned. Special earthing conductors consist of a tinned copper-stranded conductor with impregnated braiding as mechanical protection, as shown in Fig. 38, or a bare copper conductor with a lead sheath is also used.

Earthing clips are employed which must be put on bare

metal, and consist of tinned brass or copper with a terminal or lug to which the earthing wire is screwed or soldered. On ironclad apparatus an earthing lug is provided.   Continuity and earthing are safety precautions, so that in the event of the conduit becoming " alive " the fault current can leak to earth.   With a " dead earth " or " short-circuit to earth " the fuse will blow, indicating the faulty circuit, whilst smaller faults will show up on an insulation test. With poor joints the contact resistance will be high and may constitute a fire-risk due to the heat generated, so it is specified that the resistance between one point near the main switch and any other point on the conduit installation shall not exceed 1 ohm.

(2) Lead-covered Wiring

The conductors are insulated with V.I.R., the cores being of the usual colours.   With a single conductor a circular sheath of extruded lead alloy encases the insulation.   The most common type is twin-flat, consisting of two conductors, side by side, insulated from one another and covered with red and black V.I.R. to distinguish between the live wire and earthed neutral respectively. This was a popular method of installation, as the wiring was put under floors and run in plaster walls.   Care should be taken that the plaster does not cause chemical damage to the lead sheath.   A

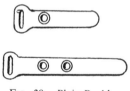

FIG. 39.—Plain Buckle Clips.

disadvantage is that nails can be driven in which will pierce the lead and short-circuit the twin wires.   As a mechanical protection, oval steel conduit or steel channel is used for running down walls.   There is a tendency for lead-covered wiring to sag unless adequately supported by fixing clips such as are illustrated in Fig. 39.   The clips are fixed by brass nails and bent over the cable, the end being threaded through the eye.   Provision must be made for continuity of the sheath where the lead has been pared off to give connecting ends. A universal bonding clamp is shown in Fig. 40. A bond-wire (or earth-wire) is run in

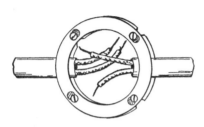

metal-sheathed and T.R.S. and P.V.C. cables and consists of a separate un-insulated conductor. There are various patented systems using special fittings which make for ease in erection and safety in opera-

FIG. 40.—Universal Bonding Clamp.

tion. Skilled labour is required to make a neat job and he cable should be carefully run off the drum, as once kinks occur they are very difficult to get out.

(3) Tough Rubber-sheathed Wiring (T.R.S.)

This consists of vulcanised india-rubber cores with an additional outer protection of tough vulcanised rubber. It was formerly called C.T.S., " cab-tyre sheathing," as the rubber casing was similar to the old cab tyres. This outer covering has greater mechanical strength and is impervious to moisture, most fumes, and reasonable steam temperatures. An advantage is that it can be erected by semi-

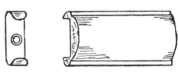

FIG. 41.—Wood Channel and Clip.

skilled labour in less time than most systems. The extra cost of the cable, compared with V.I.R. taped and braided, is compensated for by lower labour charges. Adequate support must be provided by clips or saddles or a light wooden channel which goes into a fixing clip, as shown in Fig. 41. Care must be taken to avoid sharp bends and undue pressure on the sheathing. When exposed to direct sunlight, a protective layer of weather-resisting braid should be fitted.

For continuity and earthing either a separate wire of tinned copper (14 S.W.G.) must be run to an earth-clip or T.R.S. three-core cable can be used which contains a separate earth-wire which was formerly coloured brown, but green is now specified. Such a three-core cable would have one wire red, another black, and the earth-wire green. The necessity of earthing switches and lamp-holders supplied by twin T.R.S. can be overcome by using insulated covers and dollies in the switches and shrouded insulated lamp-holders.

Thermoplastic Cable. With the war-time rubber shortage a substitute material was developed called P.V.C. (Polyvinyl Chloride). This is a synthetic, rubber-like material which is substituted for V.I.R. and T.R.S., for low (250) and medium (660) voltages. P.V.C. cables are tough and flexible at normal operating temperatures, highly resistant to burning, chemically inert, and unaffected by sunlight. As P.V.C. is thermoplastic, it should not be used under heat and pressure. The current ratings are the same as for rubber cables, published in the I.E.E. Regulations (Thirteenth Edition 1955). For conduit work P.V.C. is moulded directly on to the wire and does not need further protective coverings. With an outer protective covering of impregnated cotton braid it is suitable as a substitute for T.R.S. cables.

(4) Cleat System (Temporary)

This is often looked upon as a temporary system, but in temporary buildings both for economy and rapid construction has been much employed. The cables are insulated with V.I.R. (or P.V.C.), and must be visible throughout the run and be supported away from the wall by porcelain cleats, which are illustrated in Fig. 42, and be fitted out of reach.

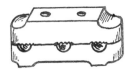

FIG. 42.—Porcelain Cleat.

Additional protection such as porcelain or metal tubes is required when passing through walls or floors. The wiring must be kept clear of gas- and water-pipes and any other metal-work.

Knob Insulators. These are employed for wiring with flexible twin wires as shown in Fig. 43 and the flexible buttons should be spaced every 3 feet for temporary wiring.

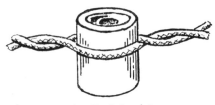

FIG. 43.—Knob Insulator.

Casing and Capping (Wood)

Many of the earlier installations were run in a wood casing with a moulded capping, as illustrated in Fig. 44. It is

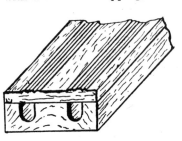

FIG. 44.—Casing and Capping.

expensive to install and needs highly skilled labour to make a good job. It can only be used in dry situations and must not be concealed in plaster or erected during building. Contact with gas-pipes and runs immediately below water-pipes must be avoided. White-wood is used for cheap jobs, but hard-woods are employed when required to match up with existing decorations. For good-class work the walls should be plugged and the casing secured by screws. The capping must be screwed on and not nailed. V.I.R. taped and braided cables are used and the grooves should not be tightly packed. Its use is not recommended.

SPECIAL SYSTEMS

" Stannos " (Hard-metal Sheathed) Cables

This consists of tinned copper conductors insulated with V.I.R. with an additional paper wrapping compressed and sheathed in tinned copper. Single cable is employed and bonding is necessary, as with lead-covered cable.

Concentric Wiring is used as an alternative to a twin conductor. It is obligatory to use the outer case as the return conductor, which must be bonded and earthed. All switches must be connected to the central conductor. " Stannos " may be used for this system, which is relatively uncommon.

Wiring in copper tube has been put forward as an alternative to steel conduit. It is less liable to internal condensation and neater in appearance, as the copper tube is thinner than steel, but the system has not attained popularity.

"Pyrotenax" Mineral-insulated, Copper-covered Wiring

This is a heat-resisting and non-inflammable system. Solid copper conductors are surrounded with compressed magnesia with an external copper sheath. Single-, twin-, and

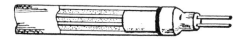

Fig. 45.—" Pyrotenax " Cable and Ferrule.

three-core cable has been made and the current rating is similar to lead-covered cables. The ends are sealed off by a special ferrule to give a water-tight and non-inflammable construction, as illustrated in Fig. 45.

Looping Out

The conventional diagram for the parallel connection of three lamps is shown in Fig. 46, from which it appears that joints would have to be made from the red and black feed

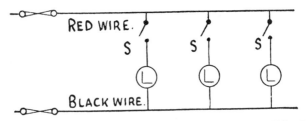

FIG. 46.—Conventional Diagram for Three Lamps in Parallel, with Switches.

wires. Such joints would have to be well made and then insulated. Such a method has long been obsolete. Instead of spending the time and labour on joints, slightly more cable is used and loops are brought down to one side

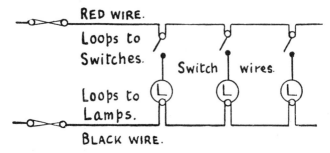

FIG. 47.—Looping Out to Lamps and Switches.

of the switch and lamp, as shown in Fig. 47. Between the other side of the switch and lamp is the switch wire, which is generally run in red. If the lamp is on a fixed bracket or lamp-holder, the black wire is taken in and out again, the loop going to one terminal. When pendent fittings are employed, the " looping in " is done at the ceiling-rose instead of the lamp-holder, which is connected to the ceiling-

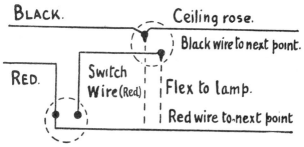

FIG 48.—Looping Out to Switch and Rose.

rose by a twin flexible cable. This is illustrated in Fig. 48, which shows how three wires enter each switch and ceiling-rose, but two of them form a loop.

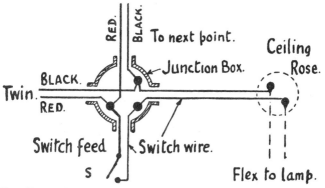

FIG. 49.—Twin-wiring Looping Out from Junction Box to Ceiling-rose.

When twin lead-sheathed cable is used, another method is employed (as illustrated in Fig. 49) which does not employ switch wires of a single conductor. Both red and black wires are fed into a junction box with four entries. Three twin cables are looped out, as indicated in the diagram ; one twin cable provides the feed to the next point, the next outlet goes to the ceiling-rose, whilst the third goes to the switch. The connections within the junction box are made

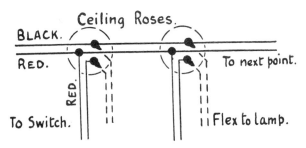

FIG. 50.—Three-plate Ceiling-roses showing Looping Out.

with brass connectors insulated from the body of the box.

Another method of looping out, using a three-plate ceiling-rose, is shown in Fig. 50, the circuit connections of which are made with pairs of wires. This method is not very common, but is used for long straight runs.

CHAPTER IV

FLEXIBLE LEADS

When apparatus is in a fixed position, then permanent cabling of a semi-rigid type can be installed, and for large installations the main service can be carried by bus-bars of copper rod or strip. But in any sized system provision must be made for connecting lamps, kettles, irons, and other portable apparatus to the permanently wired outlets. For this purpose a flexible lead is required, and these flexible leads are one of the most common points of failure, as they are often misused and are more liable to be damaged by carelessness. For household use a flexible cable with a pleasing finish is desirable, whilst workshop flexibles must be more robust without the need for the same artistic finish. Flexible leads are colloquially called "flex," and the conductor is made up of a number of fine wires twisted together and insulated with vulcanised india-rubber. With V.I.R. insulation the copper wires are tinned to prevent chemical reaction between the rubber compounds and the copper. Cheap grades of flex are poor economy and rubbishy stuff has been offered for sale. The I.E.E. Regulations for Flexible Cords are given in Table IV on page 60.

The style of finish depends upon the application, which may be glacé-cotton or artificial silk for house-wiring and impregnated cotton braiding for workshop flex.

For larger currents than given in Table IV, flexible cables going from 0·01 to 0·5 sq. inch are available.

Twin twisted flex consists of two insulated and braided conductors twisted together to form a pair.

Circular braided flex consists of insulated conductors laid up and twisted together with hemp worming to give a circular core, the whole being braided to suit the type of application.

TABLE IV

Flexible Cords

Conductor		Current Rating (subject to voltage drop) D.C. or single-phase or three-phase A.C.	Maximum Permissible Weight supportable by Twin Flexible Cord
Nominal Cross-sectional Area	Number and Diameter (in.) of Wires		
in.²		amp.	lb.
0·0006	14/·0076	2	3
0·001	23/·0076	5	5
0·0017	40/·0076	10	10
0·003	70/·0076	15	10
0·0048	110/·0076	20	10
0·007	162/·0076	25	10

For domestic use unkinkable flex is recommended. The space between the insulated conductors contains a rubber compound and heald cords for strengthening purposes, thus any pull or jerk, as when the electric iron falls off the table, does not strain the copper conductors and their insulation. The construction of unkinkable domestic flexible is illustrated in Fig. 51. The heald cords can be anchored to insulated shields or discs which are provided in good-quality fittings, as illustrated by the two-pin plug and flex shown in Fig. 52. The regulations specify that all portable apparatus, other than lamp-standards, must be fitted with circular braided flexible. Unfortunately this regulation is not always observed on portable apparatus offered for sale to the public.

Three-core Flexible

The rule regarding earthing of portable apparatus states that all exposed metal, with the exception of metal shades on insulated lamp-holders, must be earthed. For this purpose a three-core flex is used, which consists of three insulated conductors. The live conductor is coloured red and must go to the switch, if one is fitted on the appliance; the black goes to the neutral, and the green wire goes to the earthing-

Fig. 51.—Unkinkable Domestic Flexible.
(*British Insulated & Callender's Cables Ltd.*)

pin of the three-pin plug. The earthing-pin is the larger of the three pins and is often arranged to fit in the top of the socket-outlet. The method of attachment and connections are shown in Fig. 53.

E.H.—D

FIG. 52.—Two-pin Plug and Flexible Lead.

(British Insulated & Callender's Cables Ltd.)

Tough Rubber-sheathed Flexible

T.R.S. flex is employed for trailing cables and in damp positions where good mechanical protection is essential. The construction of this type of cable has already been described in Chapter III.   The present substitute for tough rubber is P.V.C. thermoplastic cable, which is similar in appearance and application.

Special flexibles for very arduous duties when subject to abrasion are protected over the tough rubber with a wire armouring.   In some cases a hard cord braiding is fitted

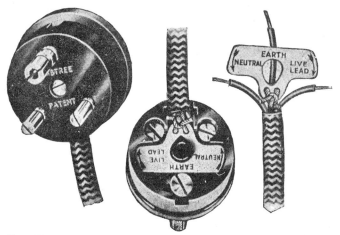

Fig. 53.—Three-pin Plug, showing Method of Attachment of Flexible Lead.

(British Insulated & Callender's Cables Ltd.)

over the outer rubber sheath, and for arduous duties a canvas reinforcement is provided between two layers of tough rubber.

Sizes of Conductors

The size of the conductors depends upon whether the cables are to be run singly or bunched together. Another limiting factor is whether they are supported in air or enclosed in a conduit or trough, as already explained.

Other considerations which affect the size to be used are :

(*a*) The voltage drop, due to the resistance of the conductor and the current it has to carry.

(*b*) The current-carrying capacity, which depends upon the type of cable and its heat-dissipating qualities.

(*c*) The minimum size of wire, which depends upon the mechanical strength and handling in use.

Voltage Drop

The effect of incorrect voltage has been dealt with in an earlier section, but here we are concerned with the effect of the cable sizes chosen upon the voltage available at the terminals of the lamp or other apparatus.

The rule for the maximum allowable voltage drop is 2 per cent. of the supply voltage plus 1 volt.

With the standard voltage of 240 this is :

$$(\tfrac{2}{100} \times 240) + 1 = 4\cdot8 + 1 = 5\cdot8 \text{ volts.}$$

On a 110-volt circuit it is 3·2 volts, so as the current per watt is then greater, larger sizes of cable must be used to keep within the permissible voltage drop.

Of this figure the 2 per cent. drop should be spread over the main cables and those forming the sub-circuits from the distribution boards in about equal proportions for economy in wiring.   The 1 volt is left for the voltage drop at contacts of distribution boards, switches, etc.   In long runs it is desirable to keep the cable sizes above the allowable drop figure.   This allows for any future extensions and growth of load and also minimises the effect of lower supply voltage which may occur at times of peak load on the supply network.   With large loads such as 3-kW electric fires or water heaters at the end of a long run, the relatively large current taken by such apparatus affects the voltage of the entire sub-circuit, so that some liberality in cable sizes is justified.   Table V on page 65 gives some of the sizes of various cables used in house-wiring. For more complete lists reference should be made to the Institution of Electrical Engineers' Regulations for the Electrical Equipment of Buildings, Thirteenth Edition 1955, or to books on electrical installation work.

The 1-volt drop is at the rated currents given which apply at a temperature of 30° C. or 86° F. Above this temperature or with larger groups of conductors the current rating is reduced as specified in the Regulations.   Paper- or cambric-insulated lead- or aluminium-sheathed cable have better

TABLE V

Current ratings for single-core rubber-, P.V.C.- or polythene-insulated cables, including tough-rubber-, P.V.C.-, lead- or aluminium-sheathed cables run—(i) bunched, and enclosed in one conduit, troughing or casing ; (ii) bunched, in free air or an open trench.

Conductor		Two Cables D.C. or Single-phase A.C.		Four Cables D.C. or Single-phase A.C.		Three or Four Cables Balanced 3-phase A.C.	
Nominal C.S.A. (in.²)	Number and Diameter (in.) of Wires	Current Rating (amp.)	Approx. Length of Run for 1-volt Drop	Current Rating (amp.)	Approx. Length of Run for 1-volt Drop	Current Rating (amp.)	Approx. Length of Run for 1-volt Drop
			ft.		ft.		ft.
0·007	7/·036	28	13	22	17	25	17
0·01	7/·044	36	16	29	20	32	20
0·0145	7/·052	43	18	34	23	39	23
0·0225	7/·064	53	23	42	29	48	29
0·03	19/·044	62	25	50	31	56	32
0·04	19/·052	74	29	59	36	67	37
0·06	19/·064	97	33	78	41	88	42

heat-dissipating qualities and can be run at a much greater current than for the cables quoted above.

Current-carrying Capacity

From the tables already given, the limitations of current for different sizes of cables according to their arrangement will be seen. The current required can be estimated and the smallest suitable size of cable can be picked out. This is generally sufficient for small-house installations, but the voltage drop can be calculated as well for the longer runs to see that it is satisfactory.

Minimum Size

The minimum size of any conductor for branch circuits is 0·0015 sq. inch, which is 1/·044 inch rated at 5 amp., and with flexible cords the minimum size is 0·0006 sq. inch, which consists of 14/·0076 and is rated at 2 amp. The resistance of small cables is given in the table below.

TABLE VI

No. and diam. of wires	1/·044	3/·029	3/·036	7/·029	7/·036
Ohm/1000 yd. at 20° C.	16·07	12·58	8·16	5·38	3·49

Voltage-drop Calculations

From Ohm's Law we know that the voltage drop = I × R, where I is the current in amperes and R is the resistance in ohms. From the load in watts (P) the current (I) can be obtained by dividing by the voltage (V), i.e. $I = P/V$. The resistance per 1000 yards of various cables is given in wire tables, so the " drop " can be calculated. All the " drops " added together, up to the apparatus concerned, should not exceed 2 per cent. of the declared voltage.

Example 10. The load on a building is 8 kW and the supply voltage is 240. If the distance from the incoming supply to the main bus-bar is 12 yards, what will be the voltage drop and the size of the two single-core cables ?

$$\text{Current } I = \frac{P}{V} = \frac{8 \times 1000}{240} = 33 \cdot 3 \text{ amp.}$$

Referring to Table V, two single-core cables of 7/·044 inch in conduit or casing will carry 36 amp. The total length of the cable, flow and return, is $2 \times 12 = 24$ yards, and its resistance per 1000 yards is 2·335 ohms. Thus the total resistance (R) is $\frac{24}{1000} \times 2 \cdot 335 = 0 \cdot 056$ ohm. Hence the volt drop is $E = IR = 33 \cdot 3 \times 0 \cdot 056 = 1 \cdot 87$ volts.

This is well within 2 per cent. of the supply voltage (4·8 V.,) but it must not be forgotten that with a building taking this load there will be other cables with some voltage drop running from the main bus-bars to sub-boards which supply the final sub-circuits.

With a number of lamps and other apparatus the total load is distributed over the length of cable from the distribution board. The farther away a point is from the distribution board the less is the current, but the greater is the cable resistance. Thus the total load can be considered as concentrated at some point along the sub-circuit cable. This " load-centre " may be the geometrical mid-point of the group or it can be found in the same way as a centre of gravity (or centroid) in applied mechanics. As a rough rule, take it as half-way along the sub-circuit route. To find the percentage voltage drop, measure the distance from the sub-board *in feet* and add up the maximum load on the branch circuit in watts. Then

$$\text{Percentage voltage drop} = \frac{PRL}{30\ V^2}$$

When P = Load on the circuit in watts.

R = Resistance per 1000 yards of the conductor used.

L = Length of lead and return, i.e. twice the route length in *feet*.

V = Declared supply voltage.

Example 11. The lamp-load on a circuit is 650 watts, and the route-length is 90 feet. If 3/·029-inch cable, having a resistance of 12·36 ohms per 1000 yards, is used, what is the percentage voltage drop on a 230-volt supply ?

Using the formula above :

$$\text{Percentage voltage drop} = \frac{650 \times 12\cdot36 \times (2\times90)}{30\times(230\times230)} = 0\cdot915\ \%$$

so the actual voltage drop is $\frac{0\cdot915}{100} \times 230 = 2\cdot1$ V.   This

is a sub-circuit, so should share the 2 per cent. drop allowed, of which it takes nearly a half, so the cable size is satisfactory.

For the five sizes of cables a convenient collection of figures is given in Table VII below, which shows the maximum length of run in feet, for 1 per cent. voltage drop on a 240-V. system.

TABLE VII

Maximum Length of Run, in Feet, for 1 per cent. Voltage Drop on a 240-volt Supply.

Load in watts		6000	5000	4000	3000	2000	1500	1250	1000	750	600	500
Current in amp.		25	20·9	16·7	12·5	8·33	6·25	5·2	4·16	3·13	2·5	2·09
Conductor												
Size	Rated current (amp.)											
1/·044	5								49	65	82	98
3/·029	10					34	45	55	68	91	114	137
3/·036	15				35	53	70	85	105	140	175	210
7/·029	20			40	53	80	107	128	160	214	267	ft.
7/·036	28	41	50	62	83	124	165	198	248	330	ft.	—

Maximum permissible current exceeded

Effect of a Heavy Load on the End of a Sub-circuit

Fig. 54 (a) shows a pair of main cables each with a resistance 0·05 ohm, and a sub-circuit with a 100-watt lamp half-way along it and another 100-watt lamp at the end. The resistance of each sub-circuit wire is 1 ohm. With the first 100-W. lamp switched on to the 110-V. supply a current of $\frac{100}{110} = 0·91$ A. flows along the main cables and half the length of the sub-circuit, the total resistance is $0·05 + 0·05 + 0·5 + 0·5 = 1·1$ ohm, so the IR drop will be $0·91 \times 1·1 = 1$ volt, thus the voltage at the first lamp will be 109 volts. When the second lamp, at the end, is switched on, it will take 0·91 A., and now the total current will be 1·82 A. from the mains. The voltage drop is $1·82 \times 1·1 = 2$ volts at the first lamp, and in addition $0·91 \times 1 = 0·91$ volts at the second lamp. Thus the voltage across the second lamp is 107·09, say 107 volts. This illustrates how the lights may be less brilliant as one proceeds along a long sub-circuit. Now suppose the occupier thinks he would like to have a 1-kW fire in the same room as the last lamp, and connects the fire to the end of the sub-circuit (see Fig. 54 (*b*)). This fire will take $\frac{1000}{110} = 9\cdot1$ amp., which is added to the existing lighting load and was never contemplated when the wiring was put in. Now let us work out the voltage across each lamp.

The total current from the mains is $9\cdot1 + 1\cdot82 = 10\cdot92$ amp. Drop to first lamp $= 10\cdot92 \times 1\cdot1 = 12\cdot01$, say 12

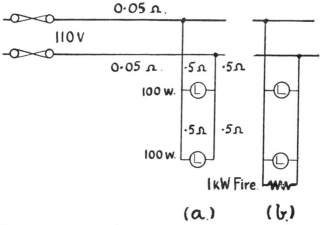

FIG. 54.—Illustrating Voltage Drop and Heavy Load on Long Sub-circuit.

volts, so the first lamp has only 98 volts across it or 89 per cent. of its proper voltage. In the remaining half of the sub-circuit the current is $9\cdot1 + 0\cdot91$, say 10 amp., and the further drop in voltage is $10 \times 1 = 10$ volts, so the second lamp has only $98 - 10 = 88$ volts across it, which is 80 per cent. of its proper voltage, so it will burn dimly. These resistance figures have been chosen somewhat on the high side to bring out this effect of a heavy load on the end of a sub-circuit, which is not good practice. The correct way is to run a separate circuit (say 7/·029) for the electric fire. This is shown in Fig. 55, in which the resistance of the wires to the fire are each taken as 0·25 ohm. We will now calculate the currents and voltages across the lamps. The main cable still carries 10·92 amp. and the drop is 1·09 volts. The drop in the wires to the fire is 9·1 A. × 0·5 = 4·55 volts, so the fire is on 108·9 — 4·55 =

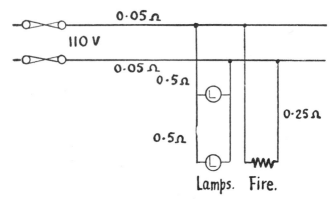

FIG. 55.—Correct Way to connect a Fire.

104·3 volts, which is not too bad. The voltage drop to the first lamp is 1·82 V., giving 110 — 1·09 — 1·82 = 107 volts, whilst the second lamp is on 107 — 0·91 = 106 volts (approx.). This compares favourably with the figures of 98 and 88 volts respectively in the former case.

Power Circuits

From the above example it is seen that power and lighting circuits should be run separately. It is generally sufficient to rate the cables for the so-called " power circuits," which supply electric fires and other heating apparatus, on a current-carrying basis, as the current taken is separate from the lighting circuits. It is not a different current of inferior quality as is sometimes imagined, due to the lower price per unit. A 2-kW. fire on 110 volts takes 18·2 amp., so that

7/·029 could be used, but for a long run use 7/·036. The same size of fire for 230 volts takes 8·7 amp., so 3/·029 is large enough. But there is a possibility of a larger fire being fitted, say 3 kW, at some later date, especially if a plug socket-outlet is provided, so 3/·036 to carry 15 amp. should be used.

For apparatus taking up to 1 kW on 200 to 250 volts, a 5-amp. plug and socket can be used, and with nothing else connected to this circuit 3/·029 has enough current-carrying capacity. For larger currents between 5 and 15 amp. there is no intermediate plug size, e.g. 2 kW at 200 volts takes 10 amp., so a 13-amp. outlet is employed and the rule is to run 15-amp. cable to match the outlet, i.e. 3/·036 is used. Considering domestic installations, the first 10 amps. of connected load must be allowed for in full, but about half to two-thirds of the remainder is reckoned in estimating the cable sizes, as all the appliances will not be on at the same time.

Lighting Circuits

These are rated at 5 amp. and either 3/·029 or 1/·044 is large enough. The former is preferable, due to flexibility and less likelihood of failure due to fracture, also the voltage drop is lower. Any 5-amp. sockets should be taken at their full value and 2-amp. outlets can be taken at $\frac{1}{2}$ amp., as a 100-watt lamp on 230 volts takes 0·44 amp.

In medium-sized houses it is not usual for more than half the lighting to be on at once, though two-thirds is sometimes taken. This should not lead to a reduction in cable size, as the wiring is already small enough for mechanical reasons. In larger buildings and institutions a larger fraction is employed.

Installation testing

In the complete installation all the wiring is tested for continuity and insulation resistance. It is a rule that the earth continuity shall have less than 1 ohm resistance. The insulation resistance of the system depends but slightly

on the grade of cable used, providing there are no breaks in
the insulation covering the wires.   Most of the leakage
current occurs at cable ends, switches, distribution boards,
and points where the connections are made.   The total
insulation resistance *decreases* with increase of length of
cable runs and with more outlets.   The rule is that the
insulation resistance of the wiring shall not be less than
50 megohms divided by the number of points.*   To test the
wiring an ohm-meter is used.   A trade name for such an

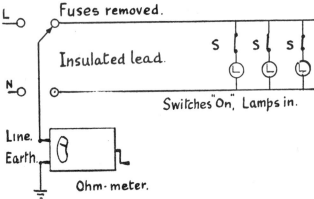

FIG. 56.—Insulation Test to Earth.

instrument made by Messrs. Evershed & Vignoles is the
" Megger," but this name is often applied in practice to all
such instruments.   The instrument consists of a hand-driven
generator which supplies a constant voltage to the installation under test.   A voltage commonly employed is 500,
i.e. twice the working voltage of the installation, though
higher values are obtainable.   There are two terminals on
the " Megger," one labelled earth and the other line.   When
the handle is driven, a constant speed is ensured by means
of a slipping clutch.   The pointer on the instrument moves
over a scale of ohms which vary from Infinity to Zero.

* Where P.V.C.-insulated cables are used 12½ megohms divided by
the number of outlets is to be used.

For the larger values Megohms or millions of ohms are marked on the scale.

With a perfect insulator, the pointer goes to Infinity, whilst with a perfect conductor, i.e. perfect continuity, the pointer goes to Zero. Thus this instrument can be used for testing insulation resistance, or continuity.

Two tests of insulation are performed, one " to earth " and the other " between conductors." Fig. 56 illustrates the insulation test to earth, which is made with all lamps and

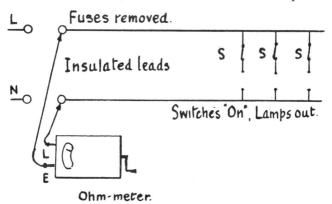

FIG. 57.—Insulation Test between Mains.

fuses in and switches on. The line terminal of the " Megger " is connected to one conductor whilst the earth terminal is connected to a good earth, such as a water-pipe (NOT a gas-pipe). The second test checks the insulation resistance between the two conductors, during which the lamps are removed, as illustrated in Fig. 57.

These tests are carried out by the Supply Undertaking before the installation is allowed to be connected to the service cable. They are a check on the safety of the wiring, but such a test, even if quite satisfactory, is not in the nature of a guarantee of the whole installation. (See section 5, I.E.E. Regulations 1955.)

It is recommended that the installation be periodically inspected and tested at intervals of not more than five years.

Earthing for Safety

The efficient earthing of the metallic casing of electrical appliances is a recognised safety precaution.

Conduit, iron switch boxes, portable apparatus, cookers, water heaters, washing machines, motors, etc., should all have a proper earth connection. This is often provided by a three-pin plug and socket or a separate earth-wire, which should be protected if liable to mechanical damage, and must be run back to a good earthing point.

In the event of any insulation becoming defective so that a current-carrying conductor comes in contact with the casing, the earth connection provides a low resistance path to earth, the large fault current will open the circuit by operating the fuses or circuit-breaker, and at the same time prevent an electric shock to anyone touching the defective apparatus. About 50 volts A.C. is the maximum pressure which a human being can withstand, but about half this value is the safe limit for animals. Alternating current is more dangerous than direct current, but the results depend upon the physical condition and the positions of the contact points.

The I.E.E. rules stipulate that the resistance between any point on the metallic casing of the installation and the main earthing point within the building shall not exceed 1 ohm.

Fatalities have occurred to persons using unearthed or faulty apparatus in bathrooms, and special precautions should be taken to see that any exposed conduit is properly earthed, and that the bath- and water-pipes are bonded to earth. Socket-outlets in bathrooms are unsafe and should not be used. Lamp-holders in the bathroom should be out of reach of a person in contact with the bath and must be of the all-insulated shrouded type. Any inside switches should be of the ceiling type or otherwise fitted outside the room, near the door.

The following example will show an earthing connection which is worse than useless.

Example 12. The end of a 1-kW. electric fire element adjacent to the " live " conductor develops a fault to the metal casing of the fire. The resistance of the fault is 5 ohms and that of the earthing circuit 15 ohms. The supply is 230 volts and the fuse fitted will blow at 20 amp. Is this apparatus safe and properly protected ?

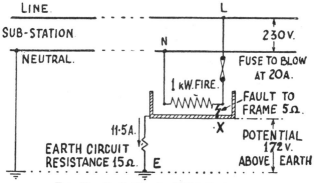

FIG. 58.—Earth Circuit of High Resistance.

The circuit diagram is given in Fig. 58, where the neutral conductor is shown earthed at the sub-station and the earth connection or electrode is denoted by E. The resistance from L to E via the fault X is 20 ohms, so the fault current is $\frac{230}{20} = 11.5$ amp.

This circuit is in parallel with the fire element, which takes a current of $\frac{1000}{230} = 4.4$ amp. The total current is 15.9 amp., which will not blow the fuse or overload the cable assuming this is 7/·029 inch to carry 20 amp. But there is 230 volts from L to E, as the resistance between E and the sub-station earth is zero, and three-quarters of this potential difference is across the points X to E, so that any person who was " earthed " and touched the frame would be liable to an electric shock at 172 volts. The calculation can be done another way : the potential *above* earth at point X is the fault current 11·5 A., multiplied by the earth circuit resistance of 15 ohms, namely, 172 volts.

It will be seen that this apparatus is most unsafe, and that the fuse only gives protection against a greater current. Suppose the fault develops into a " dead short-circuit," then its resistance falls to zero, and the fault current increases to $\frac{230}{15} = 15\cdot3$ amp., so that the total current through the fuse is now $15\cdot3 + 4\cdot4 = 19\cdot7$ amp. The fuse will heat up, and may or may not blow at once and clear the circuit, but the leakage current will raise the potential of the frame to practically 230 volts. Thus the resistance of the earth connection must be below 15 ohms for the fuse to blow.

With conduit or sheathing, i.e. when there is only one path for the current to be considered, the resistance of the earth connection must be less than that to give the fusing current when the line voltage is applied. Thus with a fuse to blow at 20 amp. on a 230-volt circuit, the resistance of the earth electrode or contact, together with the earthing conductor, must be less than $\frac{230}{20} = 11\cdot5$ ohms, but even then the earth circuit within the house must not exceed 1 ohm. Earth-fault-loop impedence tests are now specified in the I.E.E. Regulations.

The Earth-leakage Trip

Where the earth-circuit resistance exceeds 1 ohm, an earth-leakage trip must be fitted. In areas where good earthing is difficult to obtain, the use of an earth-leakage trip is imperative, and when combined with an overload device with which it is mechanically interlocked it replaces the main switch and fuses at very little additional cost for the additional protection, provided in a convenient way.

Automatic earth-leakage trips consist of a lightly set circuit-breaker which will operate with a leakage current of 0·03 amp. or 30 milli-amperes. A single-pole pattern is illustrated Fig. 59. When the leakage current reaches a

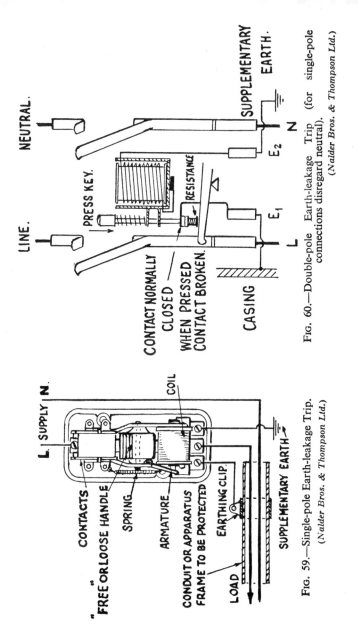

NEUTRAL.

PRESS KEY.

LINE.

RESISTANCE

SUPPLEMENTARY
EARTH.

N

E_2

E_1

L

CONTACT NORMALLY
CLOSED

WHEN PRESSED
CONTACT BROKEN.

CASING

FIG. 60.—Double-pole Earth-leakage Trip (for single-pole
connections disregard neutral).
(*Nalder Bros. & Thompson Ltd.*)

L. SUPPLY N.

COIL

CONTACTS
"FREE OR LOOSE HANDLE"

SPRING

ARMATURE

CONDUIT OR APPARATUS
FRAME TO BE PROTECTED

EARTHING CLIP.

SUPPLEMENTARY EARTH

LOAD

FIG. 59.—Single-pole Earth-leakage Trip.
(*Nalder Bros. & Thompson Ltd.*)

predetermined value, the armature is attracted and the contacts are opened. The trip is reset by means of the "free-handle," which ensures that the circuit cannot be closed against a fault. The device includes a press-key and resistance which enables a test to be carried out to see that the leakage trip is in order, and the double-pole circuit diagram is given in Fig. 60.

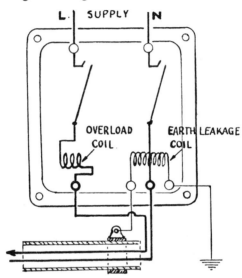

FIG. 61.—Combined Overload and Earth-leakage Trip.

(*Nalder Bros. & Thompson Ltd.*)

All trips are calibrated to operate at 22 volts (suitable for rural areas) with a resistance of 200 ohms in series with the operating coils. The main contacts are made in two sizes to carry continuously 30 or 60 amperes. The circuit diagram for a combined overload and earth-leakage trip, housed under one cover, is shown in Fig. 61. The author is indebted to Messrs. Nalder Bros. & Thompson Ltd. for the above information.

CHAPTER V

ACCESSORIES AND FITTINGS

In the last chapter we considered the main circuits ; now we have to consider the various fittings that may be employed at the ends of the sub-circuits. Good-quality accessories should be used, as the few coppers saved on inferior fittings do not compensate for subsequent failures due to the flimsy construction of cheap components.

In the house the majority of the fittings are for lighting, which may be from pendent fittings or wall brackets. Decorative tubular lighting is employed with certain decorative architectural schemes, but is beyond the scope of this book. In laying out the installation for a new house it is very desirable to settle the position of the various lighting points, so that alterations to plastering and decorations, entailing cutting out and making good, are obviated. With prefabricated construction definite channels will be provided for all services which will be an example of production planning, arrangements being made for looping out to ceiling-roses for lighting, and for power to socket-outlets and plugs.

Ceiling-roses and Plates

The first fitting commonly employed on the ceiling is a wood-block which is recessed underneath to allow for the slack ends of the wires. Care must be taken that this circular ceiling-block is screwed securely to a joist or a supporting length of wood secured between joists. The ceiling-block must never be screwed on to the laths, which tend to split and will not support the weight of the fixture. A ceiling-rose is screwed on to the block and porcelain ceiling-roses are often used. An alternative material is bakelite, and with the development of moulded products such fittings will be more common and some types do without the ceiling-block. Two connectors have grub-screws in the side which grip the looped-in wire, and extension tags carry a round-headed screw and washer. The ends of the flexible leads to the lamp go underneath the washer; the screws are then firmly tightened up. To prevent the pull coming on these terminal screws, the separate ends of the flex must be threaded through the porcelain (or bakelite) bridge-piece in between the two terminals. Take care to thread the flex through the hole of the porcelain dome before screwing down the ends. These fittings with their small screws and washers, entailing overhead work, do not encourage quick installation, so that more convenient ceiling-roses have been produced in which the flexible connections are made up before the ceiling-rose is assembled on site. A bakelite ceiling-rose with unkinkable flexible connection is shown in Fig. 62.

FIG. 62.—Bakelite Ceiling-rose, showing Method of fitting Unkinkable Flexible Lead.

(*British Insulated & Callender's Cables Ltd.*)

With conduit work, metal ceiling-plates are used which

can be mounted directly on to the lugs of a conduit box without using a wooden block. With bowl fittings a ceiling-plate with three hooks for the supporting chains should be employed. Bracket fittings should have solid back-plates, and when the supporting tubes permit, the circuit cables should be brought right up to the lamp-holder. A sufficient length of wire should be left out of the wall for this purpose.

Socket-outlets and Plugs

The British Standards Institution has laid down the standard sizes for sockets and plugs (British Standard Specifications 546 and 1363) and non-standard sizes should not be fitted. Nothing is more annoying than to find a variety of plug sizes in a domestic installation. The plugs must go well well home into the socket, so that no live metal is exposed. The use of open live two-pin plugs is to be deprecated, as they are a source of danger, especially to children. One three-pin type has shutters actuated by the earth-pin. All socket outlets in new domestic installations should be of this type and for A.C. installations comply with B.S. 1363. Three-pin plugs with earth connections must be used for all power circuits. One type of three-pin socket has a gripping arrangement which holds the plug in, unless the switch is in the " off " position, so that the plug cannot be withdrawn when the socket contacts are alive.

The standard plug and socket sizes are 2, 5, 15 and 30 amp. to B.S. 546 and the wiring to them must be for the rated current to the outlet, no matter what current is taken by the connected apparatus. Fused plugs and shuttered socket-outlets are rated at 13 amp. with fuses rated at 2, 5, 10 and 13 amp., coloured blue, grey, yellow and brown respectively to B.S. 1362.

Lamp-holders

The lamp-holders employed for domestic lighting are of the bayonet type. Two pins on the lamp go into slots, and the lamp-cap depresses two spring-loaded plungers with which the lamp-contacts make connection. Small bayonet patterns (S.B.C. or B.15) are used for special purposes, including decorative schemes. For larger sizes than 200

watts Edison screw-holders are used (Fig. 63), and the lamp-cap is provided with a screw-thread. The larger " Goliath " holders are provided with ventilating holes (not shown in Fig. 63).

Brass lamp-holders were employed for many years, but the I.E.E. regulations now specify that metal lamp-holders within 8 feet of the floor must be earthed. Metal lamp-holders can be used in metal shades and brackets which are earthed.

Fig. 63.—Edison Screw Lamp-holder.

For domestic use " all-insulated " lamp-holders made of moulded insulating material are now fitted. There is an outer shell of bakelite covering the metal reinforcement of the lamp-holder. This type of lamp-holder lasts fairly well with low-powered lamps, but the heating effect of 100-watt lamps and greater powers may cause trouble with the shade-ring, so that such lamp-holders should be inspected periodically. In all lamp-holders provision should be made for gripping the flex, so that the lamp and shade are supported without the strain coming on the wires in the terminal sockets. Bakelite lamp-holders and fittings should be periodically examined, to see that the bakelite is not cracked or

Fig. 64. — Shrouded Bakelite Lamp-holder.

chipped. If arcing or flashing occurs over the surface of bakelite, it leaves it in a dangerous condition, as carbon tracks may be formed. These give conducting paths for the current, and so its insulating properties are impaired and it is no longer safe.

Shrouded B.C. Lamp-holders are required in certain situations which are damp and steamy. The bakelite lamp-holder is fitted with a " skirt " of bakelite which screws on to the bottom of the fitting (as depicted in Fig. 64). Such shrouded lamp-holders are fitted in kitchens, sculleries, lavatories, bathrooms, and cellars, where there is any possibility of personal contact with the damp walls or ground when replacing a lamp. An alternative is to use an earthed metal lamp-holder when breakage of bakelite skirts is a possibility.

Fused Plugs and Adaptors

When it is required to connect a 5-amp. circuit to a 15-amp. plug, a fused plug is employed which contains two fuses to protect the lower current circuit. A safe design of adaptor is illustrated in Fig. 65, in which the cartridge

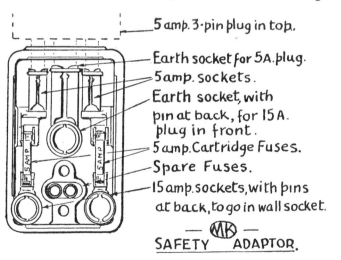

5 amp. 3-pin plug in top.

Earth socket for 5A. plug.

5 amp. sockets.

Earth socket, with pin at back, for 15A. plug in front.

5 amp. Cartridge Fuses.

Spare Fuses.

15 amp. sockets, with pins at back, to go in wall socket.

— MK —
SAFETY ADAPTOR.

FIG. 65.—Interior of Fused Adaptor.

fuses are shown. For electric clocks and radio sets plugs rated at a lower current are fitted, and these may be fused for 2 amp. or less, and such a plug is shown in Fig. 66.

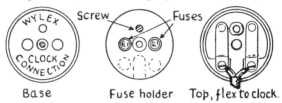

Base   Fuse holder   Top, flex to clock.

FIG. 66.—Fused Plug for Electric Clock.

Switches and Switching

A switch is a convenient piece of apparatus for opening or closing an electrical circuit, and for most domestic circuits tumbler switches are used. The single-pole switch makes or interrupts the supply on one pole or phase only; but when safety demands complete disconnection from the supply, double-pole switches are used.

Quick make and break is inherent in switch design and does not depend upon the personal element. Modern gas-filled lamps take about one-fifth of a second to attain their operating temperature, during which time the current is decreasing from about six times its steady value. A quick " make " of the switch contacts is necessary so that heating and burning does not occur. A quick " break " is required so that the arc does not linger between the switch arm and the contacts. With D.C. supplies a long break is desirable to assist in extinction of the arc, but on A.C. supplies a long arc is not desirable, though switches of this type have given satisfactory service and will be in use for some time to come. Experience with thermostats has shown that alternating currents can be efficiently interrupted by silver contacts separating at slow speed, with a very small gap of 0·025 in. The switch mechanism is simple, silent in operation without buffers or other damping devices and has a long operating life. The action is quick " make " and slow " break " but these switches must only be used on alternating current. They have replaced other silent-action switches as the only moving parts are the operating dolly and the flexing contact blade. The " Mutac " switch is illustrated in Fig. 67, and its neat design blends well with modern interiors.

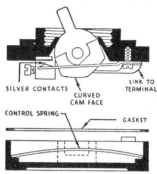

FIG. 67.—Microgap Switch.

(*General Electric Co. Ltd.*)

Types of Switches for Lighting

Tumbler switches with brass covers are now obsolete and should not be used. Moulded covers are now fitted, so that there is an insulating cover over the live parts. With sunk

FIG. 68.—" Underslung " Tumbler Switch.

(*J. A. Crabtree & Co. Ltd.*)

or flush switches with metal finger-plates the metal portion is earthed on to the conduit box, and earthed switches must be used where metal covers are employed. The standard sizes for lighting circuits is 5 amp., though they seldom have to carry this current as on 230 volts a 100-watt lamp takes 0·44 amp.

"Underslung" switches are of high electrical efficiency, the switch arm working like a pendulum in the porcelain base of the switch beneath the switch bracket. When breaking a circuit the arc is drawn between the porcelain walls of the switch base remote from the cover. This is shown in the sectional arrangement of Fig. 68.

A popular type of tumbler switch made in either "quick make and break" or "silent toggle" action is illustrated in Fig. 69.

Suspension switches (or pear-switches) are suspended by a flex from the ceiling or may form the upper portion of a switch lamp-holder. This type of switch should not be fitted when it can be avoided, as the supply voltage is on the

Fig. 69.—Surface-mounting Switch, with Moulded Dolly and Cover.
(*J. A. Crabtree & Co. Ltd.*)

conductors even when the switch is off and trouble is often experienced when the insulation of the flex becomes frayed and worn.

Ceiling-switches are preferable to the suspension switches previously mentioned. The ceiling-switch is operated by a pendent cord which is pulled either to switch " on " or " off." Such a switch is illustrated in Fig. 70. This type of switch should be used in bathrooms, in which all switches must be out of reach of a person in the bath, and is useful in bedrooms where the light is controlled from the bed. Compared with a wall-

FIG. 70.—Ceiling-switch.
(J. A. Crabtree & Co. Ltd.)

switch a considerable amount of wiring can be saved in upper-floor rooms as the switch wires down the walls are dispensed with. This is shown in Figs. 71 and 72, in which the circuits for wall-switches and ceiling-switches are compared.

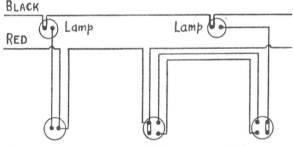

One way switch.   Two way switches.

FIG. 71.—Typical Wiring with Drops to Wall-switches.

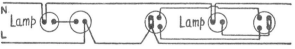

One way switch   Two way ceiling switches.

FIG. 72.—Economy in Wiring with Ceiling-switches.

Push-button switches are fitted to table-lamps and suspension switches, and have a single projecting button which is pressed for either " on " or " off " as required. Push-button switches are sometimes fitted to deep cupboards, so that when the door is opened an internal light is switched on, closing the door switching off the light.

Switching Circuits

One-way single-pole switching has been illustrated when looping in was considered, and various other switching arrangements will now be illustrated.

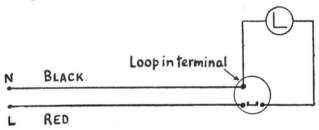

FIG. 73.—One-way Switch with " Loop-in " Terminal.

The circuit diagram illustrated in Fig. 73 shows a one-way switch with an additional " loop-in " terminal for use with surface wiring. This avoids a connector behind the block, which is bad practice. The I.E.E. Regulations have improved the conditions governing lighting outlets, so this type of switch is of interest as it provides a looping-out point for an extension, say, to a 2-amp. switch socket.

Earthed switches are made in single, two-way, and other types, in which the bridge of the switch is earthed. On one side of the switch bridge is an earthing terminal, to take an earth-wire, whilst on the other side is a brass lug which goes under the fixing screw when mounted on an earthed box (as shown in the diagram Fig. 74). Where metal covers are employed, this feature prevents possibility

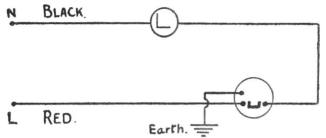

Fig. 74.—Wiring for Earthed One-way Switch.

of shock to the operator and conforms to Home Office requirements.

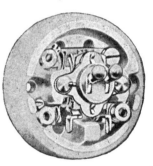

Fig. 75.—"Binob" Switch. Two one-way switch movements.

(*J. A. Crabtree & Co. Ltd.*)

The "Binob" switch is another form of one-way control in which two one-way switch movements are mounted together on one base (Fig. 75). This gives a neater arrangement than two separate switches to control two or three lamps. Fig. 76 shows two lamps independently controlled by a "Binob" switch, whilst Fig. 77 shows three lamps, of which one, two, or three can be in use at any time.

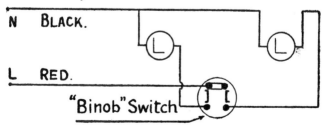

Fig. 76.—"Binob" Wiring to control Two Lamps.

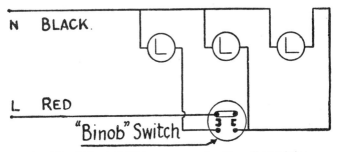

FIG. 77.—" Binob " Wiring to control a Three-light Fitting.

The double-pole switch is shown in the circuit Fig. 78. For the control of portable apparatus this switch offers the widest margin of safety to the user, as the danger of a single-pole switch in the black wire cannot occur as the apparatus is entirely disconnected from the supply when the switch is " off." Double-pole switches should be used in all situations where excessive moisture occurs.

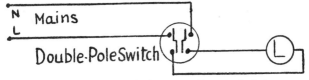

FIG. 78.—Connections for a Double-pole Switch.

Two-way Wiring. Two-way switching is a convenience, which is not generally appreciated, in bedrooms, on the staircase, corridors, and rooms with two doors. Besides convenience, such two-way switches save time and current, also accidents in the house, most of which are due to falls. A two-way switch is a single-pole change-over switch and it is possible to waste a considerable amount of cable by incorrect connection. The two best methods of wiring are illustrated in Figs. 79 and 80. The former arrangement is more economical on cable and most generally employed, though the latter is the better method. Fig. 81 shows a

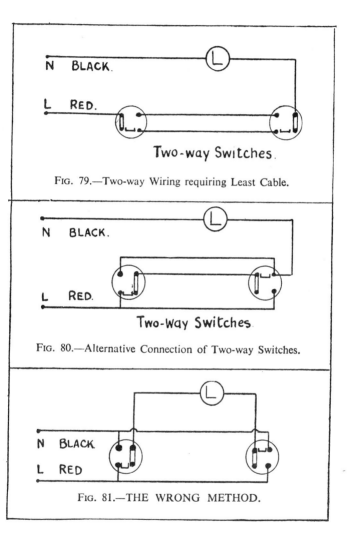

FIG. 79.—Two-way Wiring requiring Least Cable.

FIG. 80.—Alternative Connection of Two-way Switches.

FIG. 81.—THE WRONG METHOD.

wrong method of interconnecting two-way switches in which both live and neutral leads are brought into the switches. The risk of a short-circuit, especially as the circuit becomes loaded, is an ever-present risk, and if the cover is removed by anyone it is dangerous if the dolly is operated. This method is illustrated in order to emphasise its danger.

Intermediate Wiring

Long halls, corridors, and passage-ways with many doors are often wired only for two-way control when intermediate

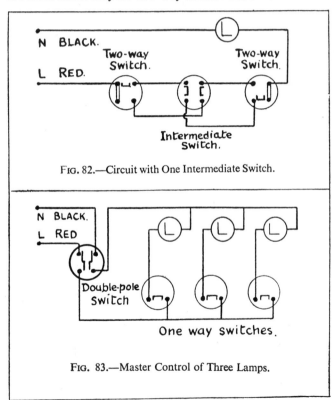

Fig. 82.—Circuit with One Intermediate Switch.

Fig. 83.—Master Control of Three Lamps.

switches put an end to " switch-fumbling " and ensure light, in front, in passages.   A circuit embodying one intermediate switch is shown in Fig. 82.

Master-control Wiring

This is not a special type of switch, but standard switches are employed.   The master switch is so connected to the circuit as to have some form of control over the subsidiary switches, limiting their action or varying their use.   Fig. 83 shows a lighting circuit with each light individually controlled by single-pole switches, but with a double-pole switch in master control of the circuits as a whole.

There are many other switching variations for special purposes, such as dimming control and restrictive lighting, but any good installation contractor can provide special circuits with suitable switches for special applications.

Lamps and Illumination

The evolution of the human eye has been a slow process, and for thousands of years outdoor conditions of large objects and daylight illumination were the normal seeing condition.   With the use of houses, some internal illumination was provided during the hours of darkness, but was of very poor quality, and reading and other close work were uncommon.   In more recent centuries the eye has been called upon to a greater extent, and in the last few generations following the Industrial Revolution the illumination provided has often been inadequate for the work in hand, whether at the factory or in the home.   Legislation has specified definite standards of factory lighting and with the present need for production great improvements have been made.   The British Electrical Development Association and the Electric Lamp Manufacturers' Association of Great Britain have published various books on the proper use of electric light for different purposes, and references should be made to them for more details than are given here.

Electric Lamps

The earliest electric light was provided by the carbon-arc, but this was not suitable for domestic use and the earliest lamps for use in houses consisted of a carbon filament in an evacuated bulb. Modern lamps have tungsten filaments, but the bulb contains an inert gas consisting of nitrogen and argon. This enables the filament to be run at a higher

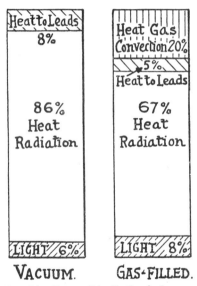

FIG. 84.—Energy Distribution in Lamps.

temperature, and gives greatly increased efficiency compared with the original carbon lamp. Even so, the light-energy is a small fraction, about 7 per cent., of the total energy, as shown in Fig. 84, which compares the energy distribution in vacuum and gas-filled lamps. With gas-filled lamps the filament is in the form of a fine coil of wire, less than a thousandth of an inch in diameter. The coil is formed in a close spiral to minimise the cooling effect of the gas. The latest development is the " coiled-coil " lamp, which is more efficient. This is due to a greater volume of incandescent metal which emits more light for the same operating temperature as a single-coil lamp. The filament arrangement is illustrated in Fig. 85.

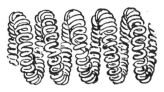

FIG. 85.—Coiled-coil Filament.

Table VIII below gives the increase of light with coiled-coil lamps, whilst coiled-coil and single-coil lamps are compared in Table IX.

TABLE VIII

Increase of Light with Coiled-coil Lamps

Watts, at 200–250 volts ..	40	60	75	100
Coiled-coil lamps, per cent. increase	20	15	$12\frac{1}{2}$	10

TABLE IX

Lumens Output of Coiled-coil and Single-coil Tungsten-filament Lamps

Type	Electric Power in Watts			
	40	60	75	100
Coiled-Coil: On 230-V. Lumens	415	700	930	1340
,, ,, Mean Spherical Candle-power	33·0	55·6	74·0	106·5
Single Coil: On 230-V. Lumens	340	600	810	1200
,, ,, M.S.C.P. ..	27·0	47·7	64·5	95·5

Mean Spherical Candle-power = Lumens/12·57.

The lumens for 100–130-volt lamps are approximately 11 per cent. higher with single-coil lamps.

Lumen. A lumen is the unit of light-flux or quantity of light. One lumen is the total amount of light falling on a surface of 1 sq. foot, every part of which is at a distance of 1 foot, from a uniform point source of 1 candle-power, i.e. a spherical surface illuminated by 1 candle-power which emits 4π lumens.

Candle-power.* The candle-power of a source is the intensity of light given out in a stated direction.

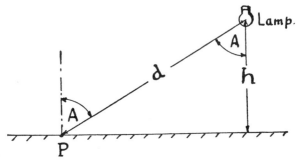

FIG. 86.—Illumination from a Lamp.

The Mean Spherical Candle Power (M.S.C.P.) is the mean of the candle-powers of a source measured in all directions.

Illumination at a Point. The illumination received at any point is inversely proportional to the square of the distance (inverse-square law) and proportional to the cosine of the angle of incidence. This is illustrated in Fig. 86, in which a lamp is suspended h feet above the horizontal plane and d feet from the lamp to the point P. The illumination (I) at point P is given by :

$$I = \frac{\text{C.P. of Lamp} \times \text{Cos A}}{d^2} \text{ foot-candles, or lumens/sq. ft.}$$

as Cos A = $\dfrac{h}{d}$, I = C.P. of Lamp × $\dfrac{h}{d^3}$ foot-candles.

* The Candela is now used.

The Foot-candle or Lumens/sq. ft. is the unit of illumination. If 1 lumen is distributed uniformly over 1 sq. foot of surface, the illumination is said to be 1 foot-candle. This unit is employed for measuring the lighting obtained, and varies from 0·00025 foot-candles for the " starlight " to 0·2 foot-candles for essential exterior work during the black-out, to interior lighting which varies from 0·5 foot-candles for passages to 50 foot-candles for precision work to a high degree of accuracy. General illumination should not be less than 6 foot-candles, whilst visual tasks such as office work and sustained reading should have 10 to 15 foot-candles for adequate seeing conditions.

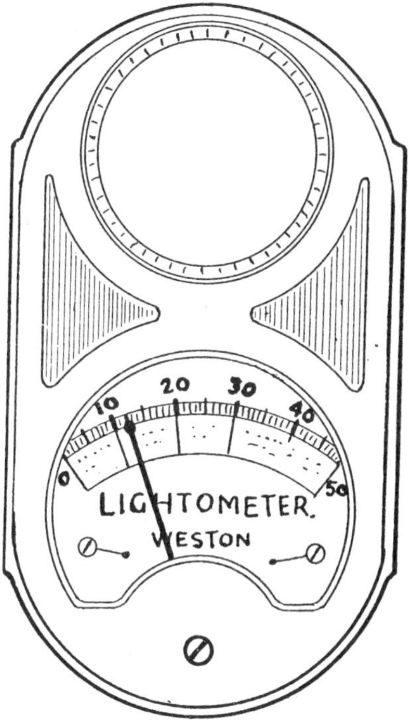

Light Measurement

The human eye is not accurate enough to measure illumination, though it can compare equality of brightness with fair

Fig. 87.—Light-meter which gives Illumination in Foot-candles.

(Sangamo-Weston Ltd.)

accuracy in photometers in which the light is compared with a standard source.

Portable photometers or light-meters are now extensively

used to give direct readings in foot-candles. Their action depends upon the effect of the light on a photo-electric cell; this generates a very small current which gives a reading on a milli-ammeter calibrated in foot-candles. Such a light-meter is illustrated in Fig. 87, and by its use measurements can be taken to check any lighting system, when installed, or at a later date to show the effect of dirt and ageing of the lamps.

Types of Incandescent Lamps—Clear and Pearl

The bulbs are made of either clear glass or with the interior frosted (pearl). The clear lamp should not be used where there is possibility of glare which will cause eyestrain. Clear-glass lamps should be enclosed in suitable shades or fittings. Pearl lamps give the same light output as clear lamps, but the diffusion obtained from the frosted glass lessens the glare and softens the shadows. Pearl lamps can be used for lower mounting heights than clear lamps, but the filament should not be visible. Opal lamps have a thin skin of opal glass on the outside of the clear-glass bulb. The diffusion is complete and shadows are minimised.

Daylight-blue lamps are of the gas-filled type with the bulb made of a blue-tinted glass. The glass absorbs some 50 per cent. of the total light, so about double the wattage is often needed. Such lamps are better than tungsten-filament lamps for colour-matching, but the light is sometimes considered cold and depressing.

Electric-discharge Lamps

The incandescent filament lamp is relatively inefficient and gives from 8 to 13 lumens per watt, depending upon its size, but it is cheap, easy to install, and can be conveniently controlled by simple switches. An electric discharge through gases gives a much greater light efficiency, Mercury and sodium electric-discharge lamps are used for street lighting and factory installations, but the single colour is a disadvantage, making them unsuitable for domestic use.

The tubular fluorescent lamp has been developed in a range of warm and cool colours, and even though more expensive in first cost than tungsten lighting, a much higher light output is obtained which is economical if these lamps are in use for comparatively long periods. The average light output for the first 5,000 hours is 52 lumens per watt for " warm white " and 45 lumens per watt for " daylight " colours of a 5-ft. lamp rated at 80 watts. The corresponding figures for a 4-ft., 40-watt tube are 54 and 48. Some colour correction is possible by a coating of suitable chemicals on the inside of the tube, but this lessens the light output.

Some auxiliary apparatus is required as shown in the circuit diagram of Fig. 88. The automatic starting switch may be of the " glow " or " thermal " type, the small condenser across it is to suppress radio interference. The starting device initiates the discharge at a high voltage but

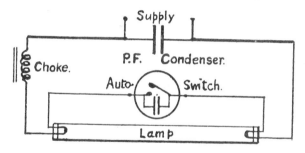

Fig. 88.—Fluorescent Lamp with Glow Starting Switch.

the final p.d. across the lamp is about 110 volts. The choke, on A.C. supplies, limits the current to the correct value but lowers the power factor so a mains condenser is fitted in parallel across the supply to improve the power factor. The 80-watt lamp requires about 7·5 microfarads and the 40-watt lamp about 3·2 microfarads. " Instant Start " lamps are available which have different control gear and an " earthing strip " along the length of the lamp which is necessary for reliable starting. Failure of the lamp is usually due to exhaustion of the active coating of the electrodes and is accelerated by frequent switching and insufficient pre-heating during starting. With relatively long running periods the life is about five times that of a tungsten lamp.

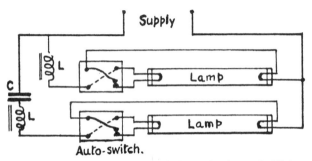

FIG. 89.—Twin Lamp Circuit. Eliminates Stroboscopic Flicker.

The electric discharge between the electrodes in the tube goes out 100 times a second on a 50-cycle supply. This causes a stroboscopic effect which in certain cases is objectionable. To overcome this a Twin Lamp circuit can be used on a single-phase supply, the circuit is show in Fig. 89. The upper lamp goes out at a different time in the cycle from the lower lamp, due to the different circuit constants, and the overall power factor is practically unity.

CHAPTER VI

DOMESTIC LIGHTING

There are three main requirements: sufficient uniform illumination, freedom from glare due to unscreened lights or reflection from polished surfaces, and freedom from deep shadows and abrupt contrasts. The light should not flicker or vary in intensity, but this is not apparent on 50-cycle systems with metal-filament lamps, as it was with the old 25-cycle systems. The choice of fittings and shades depends upon personal tastes and whether direct or indirect lighting is employed. The colour and surface of the walls have direct bearing on the effect obtained.

With direct lighting the majority of the light is projected downward by suitable reflectors, whilst in indirect lighting an opaque bowl directs all the light on to a white ceiling whence it is reflected. Indirect lighting is not used to any great extent in houses, as it needs additional local lighting and is rather cheerless. Semi-indirect lighting is employed with translucent bowl-fittings, and this gets over the glare associated with direct lighting when the shade employed often gives insufficient cut-off.

With semi-indirect lighting such as an alabaster bowl or direct lighting with large silk shades, additional plug-sockets should be provided for desk- or table-lamps and lamp-standards. In sitting-rooms where reading is done, at the dinner-table and dressing-tables, not less than 6 foot-candles should be available. In kitchens, wash-houses, and bathrooms totally enclosed diffusing fittings should be used, as the lamp is protected against steam and dirt and the exterior of the globes can be kept clean. Staircases and passages should be sufficiently illuminated so that there is not too much contrast in coming out of a well-lighted room. Extra lighting sockets should be put in at the time of installation, as they are useful for radio sets and electric clocks, if not required for lighting. Multiple plug outlets with trailing flexible leads are unsightly and extra plug-points provide a more convenient arrangement, besides giving a safer installation.

Colour. Artificial lighting differs from daylight as metal-filament lamps contain a larger proportion of red and yellow rays and are deficient in green and blue. Colours in which red and yellow predominate appear much warmer under artificial light than in daylight, whilst green and blue surfaces appear dull as they absorb much of the light. The idea that green is a restful colour is only true when ample illumination is provided, as if too much light is absorbed eye-strain is produced. With dark colours some improvement can be made, with existing installations, by decreasing the height of the fittings; but when this leaves insufficient head room, the power of the lamps must be increased or more efficient fittings can be installed.

The ratio of reflection under a tungsten lamp to that with daylight, for different-coloured papers, is given in Table X below.

TABLE X

Reflection Ratio Tungsten Lamp to Daylight

Colour of Paper	White Dif-fusing	Red	Orange	Yellow	Green	Deep Blue
Reflection under tungsten lamp Ratio reflection with daylight	1·0	1·48	1·26	1·08	0·75	0·69

The amount of reflection depends upon the surface. An enamel finish will reflect more light than a flat tone or matt surface.

Shadow. The perception of an object in three dimensions is due to the light-and-shade effect, as well as colour. There should be sufficient contrast of brightness between the object and its surroundings for easy vision, the shadows must not be dense and black but soft and grey. Heavy shadows are dangerous, as they are liable to cause accidents, especially on stairs and passages. Direct lighting gives more pronounced shadows, whilst semi-indirect lighting gives two cast shadows, one due to the light transmitted through the bowl and the other due to diffused light from the ceiling. With indirect lighting there is an absence of hard shadows, but it is the most uncommon method in domestic lighting.

Coefficient of Utilisation (or Utilisation Efficiency)

This is the ratio of the lumens received on the working plane to the total lumens produced by all the lamps in the room. Its value varies from about 0·7 to 0·1 and depends upon the polar distribution curve of the lamp, the type of fitting used, the dimensions of the room, and the colour and conditions of the walls and ceiling. Good mirrors and best white surfaces reflect about 90 per cent. of the incident light, and some approximate Reflection Factors are given in Table XI below.

TABLE XI

Reflection Factors

Material (Clean)	Approx. Reflection Factor	Material (Clean)	Approx. Reflection Factor
	per cent.		per cent.
White tile, glossy	80	Ivory, matt ..	64
White paint, glossy ..	78	Light stone ..	58
		Middle stone ..	37
Plaster, matt white.. ..	70	Yellow brick ..	35
		Red oak ..	32
Ivory, glossy ..	69	Red brick ..	25

The coefficient of utilisation is modified by the room proportions. Mounting height of lamps and complete tables are given in more detailed works on Illumination.

Table XII gives some values of room indices and directions as to their selection.

TABLE XII

Room Index

Classify the room according to the proportions and the mounting height above the working plane. Use the upper column headings for direct, semi-direct, and general lighting ; for semi-indirect and totally indirect fittings use the column at the bottom of the table.

Room width. Feet	Room length. Feet	Direct, Semi-direct, and General Fittings		
		Height of Fitting above Working Plane		
		5 feet	10 feet	14 feet
8	10 12 16 24	A* A* B B	* The room index so marked should be advanced by two letters when only a single fitting is used, e.g. A advanced to C.	
10	10 14 20 30	B* B* B C		
12	12 18 24 35	B* B* C C	A A	
16	16 30 50	C* D D	A* B B	A
20	20 40 60	D D D	B B C	A A B
		7½ feet	15 feet	21 feet
		Ceiling height above working plane		
		Semi-indirect and Indirect Lighting Fittings		

The dimensions of a room affect the utilisation efficiency as in a small room a greater proportion of the light is absorbed by the walls, whereas in a large room lamps in the centre portion will throw practically all their light on the working plane.

Effect of Walls and Ceiling

The colour and surface of the walls have considerable effect on the illumination on account of their reflecting power. The lighter the colour of the walls and ceiling the more the light reflected, and consequently the higher the coefficient of utilisation. Allowing a small proportion for deterioration, wall-paper colours can be arranged as below in three classes. Light with more than 50 per cent. reflection, medium with 35 per cent. reflection, and dark with 20 per cent. reflection. The colours are arranged in order of reflecting power, and this should be taken into consideration when deciding the total light required.

Light: white, cream, chrome yellow, light orange, light grey.

Medium: yellow, light pink, light buff, light blue.

Dark: light green, light brown, red, dark green, maroon, blue.

Ceilings are generally white or cream and can be divided into very light with 70 per cent. reflection and fairly light with 40 per cent. reflection.

The effect of smoke and dirt will lessen these figures and coloured ceilings will give lower values.

Depreciation Factor.* This allows for the falling off of efficiency due to deterioration of reflectors, walls and ceilings caused by dirt and the ageing of lamps. An allowance of 15 to 30 per cent. loss of efficiency is allowed, giving depreciation factors of 1·18 and 1·43 respectively.

Table XIII gives examples of different types of lighting and shows how the coefficient of utilisation can be obtained. These five sections should meet most domestic applications.

The typical lighting fittings are illustrated in Fig. 90 by

* Maintenance Factor is now used which is the reciprocal of Depreciation Factor.

(I.) DIRECT
Open Reflectors
High efficiency

(II.) DIRECT, with globe
Lessens glare
Better appearance

(III.) SEMI-DIRECT
Enclosed fitting with
some light upwards

(IV) GENERAL. Enclosed
Diffusing fitting
gives soft shadows

(V.) SEMI-INDIRECT
Enclosed or Bowl
Major light upwards

FIG. 90.—Typical Lighting Fittings.

TABLE XIII
Coefficient of Utilisation
Find Room Index from Table XII. Estimate Reflection Factor with Colour Chart Table XI

Light Fitting	Ceiling	Fairly Light 40 per cent.		Very Light 70 per cent.	
	Walls	Fairly Dark 25 per cent.	Light 50 per cent.	Fairly Dark 25 per cent.	Light 50 per cent.
	Room Index	Coefficient of Utilisation			
(i) **Direct** Open reflectors, 70 per cent. light downwards	A	·39	·43	·39	·44
	B	·43	·46	·43	·47
	C	·50	·53	·50	·54
	D	·55	·58	·56	·59
(ii) **Direct** Reflectors with enclosed globe, 60 per cent. light downwards	A	·24	·27	·25	·29
	B	·27	·30	·28	·32
	C	·31	·33	·32	·36
	D	·35	·36	·36	·40
(iii) **Semi-direct** Enclosed fittings with major light downwards, 55 per cent.	A	·25	·29	·26	·31
	B	·28	·32	·29	·34
	C	·34	·38	·36	·41
	D	·37	·42	·41	·45
(iv) **General** Enclosed diffusing fitting, 45 per cent. light downwards	A	·20	·24	·23	·28
	B	·23	·27	·26	·32
	C	·29	·32	·33	·38
	D	·32	·36	·37	·43
(v) **Semi-indirect** Enclosed fitting, major light upwards, 55 per cent.	A	·11	·15	·16	·20
	B	·13	·17	·18	·23
	C	·17	·22	·24	·28
	D	·20	·25	·28	·33

simple diagrams, but artistic domestic shades may give results which differ from the calculated values.

The lumens obtained from 200- to 250-volt tungsten lamps ranging from 40 to 500 watts are given in Table XIV.

With 100- to 130-volt lamps about 11 per cent. higher values are obtained.

Electric-discharge lamps give from 30 to 50 lumens per watt, but more complete data are published by the manufacturers of these lamps.

TABLE XIV

Nominal Average Lumens throughout Life. 240-V. clear and pearl lamps.

Watts ..	40	60	75	100	150	200	300	500
Lumens	390	665	880	1260	1960	2720	4300	7700

To ascertain Lamp Size

Lumens per lamp =

$$\frac{\text{Foot-candles} \times \text{area per lamp sq. ft.} \times \text{depreciation factor*}}{\text{Coefficient of utilisation}}$$

Find the size of the lamp from Table XIV to give approximately the number of lumens required. Choose the larger rather than the smaller size.

An example will now show the application of this method.

Example 13. A sitting-room 8 feet by 11 feet has a single lamp which gives direct illumination and is fitted 5 feet above the working plane. The walls are fairly dark and the ceiling is very light. Assume a depreciation factor of 1·18. What size lamp is required for an illumination of 6 foot-candles (lumens/sq. ft.) ?

Area per lamp is 88 sq. feet. From Table XII the room index is A, but for a single fitting this is advanced to C. From Table XIII (i), starting at room index C, the third column along gives 0·50 as the coefficient of utilisation.

$$\text{Lumens per lamp} = \frac{6 \times 88 \times 1\cdot18}{0\cdot5} = 1250.$$

From Table XIV a 100-watt lamp gives 1260 lumens, and this size of lamp is the minimum which should be used, as with further loss of efficiency and a depreciation factor of

* If Maintenance Factor is used instead of Depreciation Factor it appears in the denominator.

1·25, 1325 lumens are required for an illumination of 6 foot-candles. For dining-rooms and sitting-rooms the average value of illumination should be from 6 to 10 lumens/sq. ft., so the above value is not excessive and further local lighting is desirable for reading or sewing, which needs from 10 to 20 lumens/sq. ft. With larger rooms, especially dining-rooms with serving sideboards, more than one lighting fitting is necessary from the ceiling, unless socket-outlets are provided, as wall fittings are often more ornamental than useful.

In drawing-rooms the average value should be from 6 to 10 lumens/sq. ft., but sufficient outlets should be provided for standard or table-lamps and a piano should be so illuminated that the player does not cast a shadow on the music.

Bedrooms require about 5 to 7 lumens/sq. ft. One light should be in front of the dressing-table and between the user and the mirror, about 7 feet from the floor. Additional outlets should be provided for bed-lights and fitted basins. A separate central light for the wardrobe is often useful, especially if it contains a long mirror. Two-way switching should be employed, so that the main light can be switched on at the door and off from the bed-side. For the latter switch one of the ceiling type is preferable to a pear-switch.

Bathrooms, toilets, and wash-rooms should have protected fittings either of the enclosed type or, at least, lamp-holders with skirts. The switches should be outside the door and persons in contact with the bath must not be able to reach wall-switches. This gives another useful and safe application for ceiling-switches. Socket outlets must not be provided in bathrooms.

Kitchens require at least 7 lumens/sq. ft., and it is very desirable to provide enough light at the cooker, sink, and work-table, as the following example will show.

Example 14. A kitchen 9 feet 9 inches by 9 feet 9 inches is provided with two semi-direct enclosed fittings mounted adjacent to the ceiling, which is $7\frac{1}{2}$ feet above table-level. Each fitting contains a 230-volt 60-watt lamp, giving 700 lumens. The ceiling and walls are of a light colour and the maintenance factor is 0·8. Estimate the illumination provided.

The layout of the kitchen is given in Fig. 91. The two lights are arranged diagonally, so that the cooker, sink, and fitted cabinet with its work-table are illuminated. Switches are provided at each door, as shown on the plan, and control the adjacent lamp.

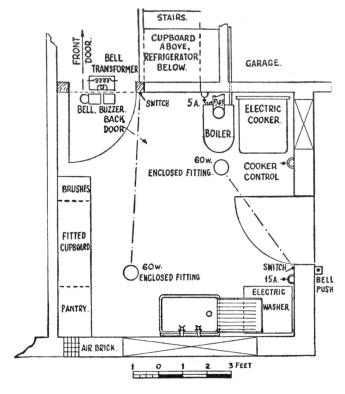

FIG. 91.—Layout of a Kitchen.

The room index is B, as for a 10-foot × 10-foot room, and the coefficient of ulitisation is 0·34, from (iii), Table XIII.

$$\text{Area/lamp} = \frac{9\frac{3}{4} \times 9\frac{3}{4}}{2} = 47\cdot5 \text{ sq. feet.}$$

Lumens/sq. ft. =

$$\frac{\text{Coeff. of utilisation} \times \text{lumens/lamp} \times \text{maintenance factor}}{\text{Area/lamp}}$$

$$= \frac{0\cdot34 \times 700 \times 0\cdot8}{47\cdot5} = 4 \text{ lumens/sq. ft.}$$

This figure is too low and a 100-watt lamp should be used in each fitting. This would bring the illumination up to 7·2 lumens/sq. ft.

Sculleries and wash-houses should have a light over or beside the sink and not behind the person using it. The switches should be outside the door and not adjacent to the sink or within reach of wet hands. Protected fittings are best for damp situations, but in any case the lamp-holders must be shrouded, i.e. fitted with skirts.

Halls and staircases should have from 2 to 4 lumens/sq. ft. with a mean value of 3 lumens/sq. ft., and the light should show the treads of the stairs and any changes of level.

Layout of Lighting

The lighting should be considered from the arrangement of the various rooms. The switches should not be behind doors or in awkward positions just to save a few feet of wiring. Whenever possible the position of lighting-points and switches should be selected before the wiring is commenced. This is particularly important with sunk work if cutting-out and making good is to be avoided ; such alterations with re-plastering often cause unsightly discoloration of the wall-paper. The occupier should be consulted, if possible, but experience and common sense should be used to temper any fantastic schemes. If a plan of the house is available, the details should be laid out on this ; and failing

No.	Description.	Graphical Symbol.	No.	Description.	Graphical Symbol.
	Group 8A. Points (Various)			Group 8C. Local Switches.	
8A1	Ceiling Point, Lighting.	○	8C1	1-way Switch.	
8A2	Ceiling Point, Power.	◎	8C2	2-way Switch.	
8A3	Floor Point, Lighting.		8C3	Intermediate Switch.	
8A4	Floor Point, Power.		8C4	Pear Switch for Lighting.	
8A5	Bracket Point, Lighting.			Group 8D. Fuse Boards, Main Switches, Cut-outs and Meters.	
8A6	Fan Point.		8D1	Main Fuseboard without Switches, Lighting.	
8A7	Synchronous Clock Point.		8D2	Main Fuseboard with Switches, Lighting.	
8A8	Special Purposes Point.	⊗	8D3	Main Fuseboard without Switches, Power.	
	Group 8B. Wall Sockets.		8D4	Main Fuseboard with Switches, Power.	
8B1	Lighting, Wall-socket.		8D5	Main Switch, Lighting.	
8B2	Lighting, Wall-socket and Switch combined.		8D6	Main Switch, Power.	
8B3	Power, Wall-socket.		8D7	Main Cut-out, Lighting.	
8B4	Power, Wall-socket and Switch combined.		8D8	Main Cut-out, Power.	
8F3	Telephone Point, Internal.	▲	8D9	Meter.	○
8F4	Telephone Board, Internal.	△	8D10	Distribution Fuseboard without switches, Lighting.	
8H3	Loud Speaker Outlet.		8D11	Distribution Fuseboard with switches, Lighting.	
8H4	Earth Point.		8D12	Distribution Fuseboard without switches, Power.	
			8D13	Distribution Fuseboard with switches, Power.	

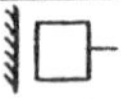

Fig. 92.—British Standard Symbols.

this, a sketch-plan should be drawn approximately to scale.

The service cable will be arranged by the Supply Undertaking, and their fuses and meters should be adjacent to the point of entry, but should not take up valuable cupboard or pantry space. With some modern houses the garage is often convenient for this ; but if this is not so, a special cupboard or inset recess can be provided which will also house the main distribution boards for lighting, power, and other purposes.

Symbols for Plans

British Standard Graphical Symbols are given in British Standard Specification No. 108 (details of all specifications can be obtained from the British Standards Institution, 28 Victoria Street, London, S.W.1). Section 8 deals with interior wiring installations and is illustrated in Fig. 92. These symbols are used on the plans of the houses which illustrate two installations, in Chapter VIII. B.S. 108 : 1951 modifies some of these symbols.

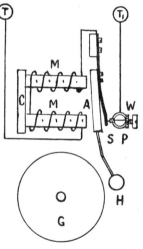

It will often be found that architects and installation engineers employ their own symbols, especially on small-scale plans.

ELECTRIC BELLS AND INDICATORS

The trembling bell is a simple piece of electromagnetic apparatus ; the working principle is illustrated by the skeleton circuit diagram of Fig. 93. The electro-magnet consists of an iron core, C, which is easily

FIG. 93.—Internal Connections of Electric Bell.

magnetised when the current traverses the magnet coils, MM, but when the current ceases the iron loses its magnetism. One end of the magnet coils is connected to terminal T, whilst the other terminal, T_1, is connected to an insulated brass pillar, P, which carries an adjustable contact-screw, W. The tip of the screw makes contact with the spring, S, when the circuit is completed, by pressing the bell-push. The current around the winding, MM, causes the iron core to be magnetised and the armature, A, is attracted. This breaks the contact with the spring, S, the current in the coil ceases, the magnets lose their magnetism, and the armature flies back. The action is then repeated. This gives a trembling movement to the hammer, H, against the gong, G. Various types of gongs, either of bell-metal or steel wire, can be obtained to give distinctive notes ; but if a quieter note is required a buzzer can be fitted. Sources of trouble in a bell or buzzer are generally due to a fault in the contact-breaker, either by weakening of the spring or corrosion of the contact-screw. Sometimes a breakage may be found in the internal wiring of the bell.

A buzzer works on the same principle as the trembling bell, but the hammer and gong are absent. The vibration of the contact-breaker, which is made relatively light, gives the characteristic high-pitched note.

A good quality bell or buzzer should be obtained with the components mounted on a hard-wood base with a well-fitting cover to keep out dust. Bells of the bakelite-moulded pattern are now often preferred and are made suitable for either low- or high-voltage operation. In the latter case better insulation is required and the contact-breaker must be more robust.

Continuous-action Bells

These are bells which continue to ring after the distant bell-push or contact is released and only cease when the local battery is exhausted or the operating cord is pulled. The local battery circuit is shown in Fig. 94, together with the additional mechanism. With the first movement of the armature, A, the trigger, U, disengages from the projection on the end of the armature and makes contact with the auxiliary pillar, X. The bell is then directly connected to the local battery, as will be seen from the circuit diagram. When the operating cord is pulled down, the trigger again engages with the projection on the end of the armature, the original connection is restored, and the local battery circuit is broken.

Bell-pushes of many types are on the market, and here again the best is desirable. For outside situations the metal-barrel type should be used, whilst for bedside positions the pear

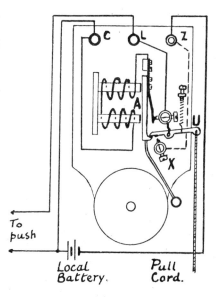

FIG. 94.—Continuous-ringing Bell.

push-or-pull type is more convenient than the flat type and allows the wiring to be carried out above the ceiling. For special purposes door, window, and floor contacts are used, as well as burglar alarms with concealed wiring, but the reader is referred to an electrical catalogue for such special items.

Relays

A relay is used to close a local battery circuit connected near the bell when the current from a distant push would not

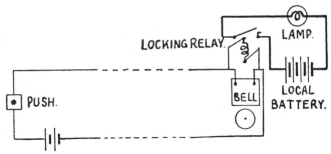

FIG. 95.—Luminous Call System with Relay.

be strong enough to ring the bell. Relays are also used with luminous call systems, the signal being sent by the distant push which rings the bell and the locking-relay connects the local battery to the lamp; this remains alight until reset. The circuit diagram is given in Fig. 95.

The relay consists of a delicate form of electro-magnet with finely adjusted contacts. They are also used with pendulum indicators in large establishments with long runs, as shown in Fig. 96, which gives a four-point indicator circuit with separate relays and a local battery.

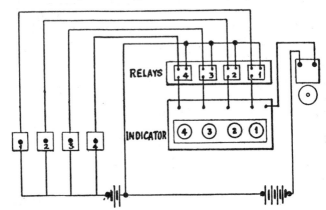

FIG. 96.—Four-point Indicator with Separate Relays.

PLATE 1. Night storage heater with wrought iron metal frame as shelf space

Photo: General Electric Co.

PLATE 2. Four ring electric cooker, with automatic oven timer

Batteries for Electric Bells

A battery is a group of cells joined up to give greater power; they are generally connected in series, so that the individual voltage of each cell is added to the next one, as already explained in Chapter II. Cells of different sizes should not be connected together, as their internal resistances differ. The Leclanché cell is generally used for bell work, and in both the wet and dry form the chemical constituents are the same. The wet Leclanché cell consists of a glass jar containing a solution of sal-ammoniac (ammonium chloride), in which stands a porous pot with a central carbon plate which is surrounded by the depolariser. The terminal on the carbon is the positive, whilst a zinc rod in the electrolyte is the negative connection. Wet cells are best kept in a cool place as evaporation is minimised; dry cells, on the other hand, are better in a slightly warm situation. The dry cell has the same chemical constituents as the wet cell, but the chemical paste, which takes the place of the sal-ammoniac solution, cannot be renewed; also the outer zinc case gets perforated due to the chemical action and cannot be replaced like the zinc rod of the wet type. An inert cell is a form of dry cell which can be stored for long periods without deterioration. When required, a little water is introduced into a vent-hole, so moistening the chemical paste. The e.m.f. of these cells is about 1·5 volts; it falls if much current is taken from them, depending upon their size, but they are quite satisfactory for intermittent work. Where larger currents are required, a lead-acid accumulator is used which has to be charged from a d.c. supply, or with a.c. supplies a trickle-charger can be used, though in the latter case a bell-transformer is preferable.

Electric Bells on A.C. Supplies

The magneto-bell is operated on low-frequency alternating current, but as it is confined to telephone installations it is beyond the scope of this book. With 230-volt 50-cycle supplies a bell transformer is used. *This should be of the double-wound type*, in which the two windings are entirely separate and insulated from one another.   Fuses should be fitted to protect the primary (230 V.) winding, whilst one terminal of the secondary winding and the iron core should be earthed.   If a metallic shield is fitted between the windings, this should also be earthed.   With two bell-pushes, one at the front door and the other at the back door, the low-voltage winding can be connected via the respective pushes to a bell and a buzzer, instead of using an indicator, as shown in Fig. 91, where the bell-transformer, bell, and buzzer are shown mounted above the kitchen door.

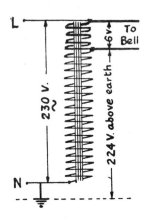

FIG. 97.—Auto-transformer incorrectly connected.

Auto-transformers, which consist of a single winding on an iron core, should not be used, as the low-voltage winding is not entirely separate and insulated from the main supply. The low-voltage end should be adjacent to the neutral connection, and Fig. 97 shows an auto-transformer *incorrectly connected* and the dangerous condition it creates.   The live conductor is shown connected to the common terminal for both high- and low-voltage sections, and it will be seen that, even though there is only 6 volts (assumed) across the bell circuit, this circuit is at least 224 volts above earth.   This voltage is dangerous both to the low-voltage bell-wiring and to any user of the bell.

Indicators are provided to show from which room a bell has been rung.   There are three types of movement—Pendulum, mechanical, and electrical replacement.   Of these the first is the simplest and consists of a pendulum with an iron armature which is attracted by an electro-magnet. This is illustrated in Fig. 98, which shows the circuits using a bell-transformer. The mechanical-replacement movement has a resetting rod projecting from the side of the indicator case, whilst the electrical-replacement type is reset by a push which can be connected either adjacent to the indicator or at a convenient point some distance

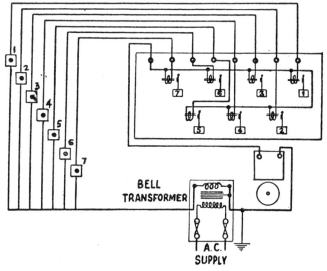

FIG. 98.—Bell-transformer and Indicator Circuits.

away. Some indicators include a bell with the movement enclosed under the gong, which is mounted in a neat manner on the top of the case.

Bell-wiring. Good materials and careful installation are essential if the bell system is to be reliable. Conduit or surface wiring can be used. If the wiring is buried in the wall it should be protected by bell-tubing. The size of copper wire should be 20 S.W.G., though 22 S.W.G. can be used for short runs. Twin bell-wire, double cotton covered, of two different colours (which has been waxed), is often used for internal wiring, but if a single wire is used, do not forget that there is a " flow " and " return." The length of wire required should include corners and recesses. Kinks in the wire must be avoided or the single-stranded conductor may break at some future date. For the best-quality work, especially in damp situations and outdoor work, twin lead-covered wire should be used. Brass saddles which do not cut into the insulation are preferable; but if staples are used, they should have an insulating saddle made of fibre, with a well-rounded top to the staple. Bell-wiring should be kept separate from lighting and power circuits, and must not be run in the conduit carrying these circuits.

There are many other arrangements of bell-circuits which are made up to suit special requirements, and when there is a considerable distance between bell and push an " earth return " is sometimes used to economise wire, using earth-plates or water-pipes. Gas-pipes must never be used for earthing connections. For signalling purposes, single-stroke bells are used, or special pushes which operate like a Morse key are fitted often with a single-line wire and earth return.

CHAPTER VII

ELECTRIC SPACE-HEATING

The open coal fire will still be used in living-rooms on account of its cheerfulness, but it is not generally appreciated that only some 25 per cent. of the heat-energy of the coal effectively warms the room.

Assuming that when 1 lb. of coal is burnt 12,000 B.Th.U. are liberated, only about 3000 B.Th.U. are radiated into the room.

One kilowatt-hour or one unit of electricity is a constant quantity in all localities, and the quantity of heat contained in one unit is 3412 B.Th.U.,* and the efficiency of conversion to heat is 100 per cent. at all loads.

Judging by appearance, space-heating equipment can be divided into the radiant type in which there is a warm glow, such as the popular "electric fire," and the luminous lamp radiator which is now obsolete.

Fig. 99.—Combined Radiant and Convector Heater.

(English Electric Co. Ltd.)

* The British Thermal Unit (B.Th.U.) is the quantity of heat required to increase the temperature of 1 lb. of water by 1° F.

The dark type of heaters include convectors, hot-water radiators, tubular heaters, and panel heaters, which provide the necessary warmth in an efficient manner but without the bright radiation of the electric fire. Combined radiators and convectors give the advantage of radiant heat with space-heating by the circulation of warm air. This type of combined heater is illustrated in Fig. 99. The appearance of warmth is obtained by an amber illuminated panel in the

FIG. 100.—2 kW Reflector Fire.
(*General Electric Co. Ltd.*)

base, and a brightly lit grille at the top, through which the warm air is circulated. This model uses two or one units per hour, controlled by the switch at the base.

A modern-style fire providing a direct radiated heat at the correct level for warmth and comfort is illustrated in Fig. 100. Safety guards must now be fitted to all electric fires to comply with B.S. 1670 and 1945 and with the Heating Appliances (Fireguards) Regulations, 1953. All portable fires are fitted with 6 feet of 3-core flexible cord.

A 1-kW fire designed for wall or floor mounting is shown in Fig. 101. Such a fitting is useful in the bathroom, but it must be mounted high up on the wall out of reach of a person in contact with the bath.

Size of Fires for Various Rooms.

Size of Room (cu. ft.)	Dining Room, Lounge or Hall	Bedroom, Kitchen or Bathroom
750/1000	1–1½ kW	1 kW
1250/1500	2 kW	1½–2 kW
2000	3 kW	2 kW

FIG. 101.—1-kW Swivelling Electric Fire, Portable or Wall Mounting.
(*General Electric Co. Ltd.*)

Convector-heaters run at a lower temperature than the elements of an electric fire, so that the elements have long life and require no maintenance, and they are essentially safe from fire-risk. They are more suitable for continuous use for space-heating, as it takes some time for the warm air to be circulated compared with the immediate local effects of radiant-fire heating.

Thermostatic control should be employed, both to conserve fuel and to maintain a reasonably constant temperature. The mercury-in-glass thermostats will operate on either D.C. or A.C. supplies, but the bi-metal strip type is suitable only for A.C. The construction of the heating element and arrangement of " Electric Vectairs " is shown in

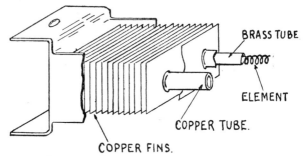

FIG. 102.—Construction of " Electric Vectair."

(*British Trane Co. Ltd.*)

Fig. 102. The element consist of a coil of resistance wire set in a refractory compound encased in a brass tube. These, in turn, are fitted inside a larger tube of copper which has first been expanded through copper fins spaced at six to the inch, thus forming additional heating surface giving a rapid heat transfer to the air. The complete " Vectair " unit is fitted into a steel cabinet having an inlet space at the bottom and an outlet grille at the top. Individual thermostats can be built in above the element, or a separate wall-mounting thermostat can be used. In modern buildings the convector units can be concealed in the walls or in the window space, thus presenting a smooth exterior surface, as illustrated in Plate I, facing page 52, and Plate II, facing page 53. The loading in watts varies from 500 to 3000 ; the latter size requires wiring for 15 amp. (3/·036 minimum) and one thermostat is sufficient for this load.

Tubular Heaters. This type of heater warms a room largely by radiation, though some convection occurs, and consists of a circular steel tube about 2 inches diameter, though in some types the tube is oval in section, which gives a greater radiating surface for a given volume. The lengths of the tubes vary in standard sizes from 2 feet to 17 feet and are supported by wall-brackets or floor-mountings.

The heating element inside the tube consists of a nickel-chrome element which runs at black heat and is supported on mica insulators. One end of the tube is closed by a steel cap, whilst the other end carries a terminal assembly which carries two brass terminals connected to the element and a brass earthing terminal solidly connected to the tube. The standard loading is 60 watts per foot run, but elements for 80 watts per foot run are also made. With 60 watts per

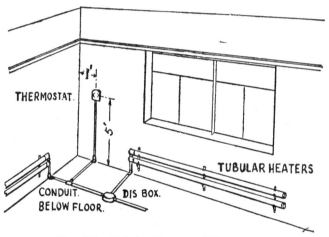

FIG. 103.—Tubular Heaters and Thermostat.

foot run the B.Th.U.s per foot are 205 with a surface temperature of 200° F., whilst with 80 watts per foot run the B.Th.U.s per foot are 273 with a surface temperature of 265° F. Thermostats should be employed to keep the temperature constant and save waste of current, and if desired time-switches can be supplied to switch on the heat at certain times. Fig 103 shows the arrangement of two double banks of tubular heaters with connections to conduit under the floor and a thermostat in the corner of the room. The heaters should be around the skirting under windows,

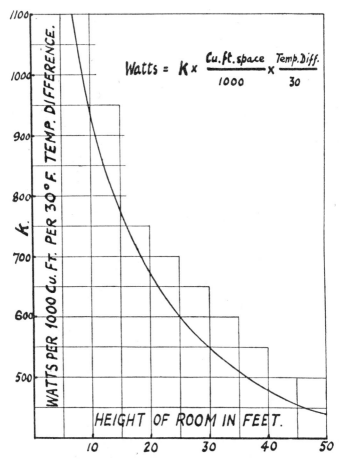

FIG. 104.—Space-heating Graph.

to minimise the effect of down draughts and cold-air inlets.

To calculate the Heat required

The design of the complete heating installation with any

degree of accuracy is a matter for expert and laborious calculation, but the following approximate method is useful for estimating the electrical load. The graph given in Fig. 104 enables calculations to be made for normal buildings when the window-glass area is not more than 20 sq. feet per 1000 cu. feet. The height of the room being known, the watts per 1000 cu. feet of space can be obtained from the graph for a temperature difference of 30° F. between the inside and the outside of the building, and a proportional figure will apply for other temperature differences. Allow either 60 watts per foot run of tubular heater or 80 watts per foot run where a higher surface temperature is permissible.

A recent survey states that 60 per cent. of all consumers had one or more space-heaters representing an installed load of 17 000 MW on the C.E.A.

Example 15. A small bedroom $10 \times 8 \times 11$ feet is to be warmed to an inside temperature of 50° F., with the outside temperature 35° F. What length of tubular heater, run at 80 watts per lineal foot, would be required, and what would be the total cost of energy for 1000 hours per annum at 1d. per unit ?

Size of room $= 10 \times 8 \times 11 = 880$ cu. feet.

Temperature difference $= 50 - 35 = 15°$ F.

From graph for 11-foot height, $K = 890$.

$\therefore$ watts $= 890 \times \frac{880}{1000} \times \frac{15}{30} = 392$.

At 80 watts/foot-run, length required is 5 feet, taking 400 watts.

Total number of kWh $= \frac{400}{1000} \times 1000 = 400$.

Total cost at 1d. per unit $= 400 \times$ 1d. $=$ £1 13s. 4d.

Panel Heaters

There are two main types : (*a*) high-temperature panels, which work at a surface temperature of approximately 400° F., and (*b*) low-temperature panels, which operate at much lower temperatures from about 200° F. for wall panels to about 70° F. for floor panels. The former type are not embedded in the walls or ceilings, but are suspended or mounted on inclined brackets so that the radiant heat is directed downwards. The latter type can be fixed against a wall or be embedded in either walls or ceiling. With the lower temperatures the backs of the panels do not transfer too much heat to the structure and heat-insulating pads are not always necessary, though they are desirable on outside walls. Thermostatic control should be employed with either type, and as the diversity of the load varies with the conditions, the main cables should be large enough to deal with the total current.

Position of Thermostats

The function of a thermostat is to maintain an equable temperature as well as to conserve electrical energy. They should be freely exposed to air but not directly subjected to radiant heat or draughts. If thermostats are fitted too close to the floor they are in the paths of cold draughts, especially if near to the side of the door which opens. The warm air increases in temperature towards the ceiling, so if a thermostat is set at, say, 65° F. and is placed too low, then the mean temperature of the room at the higher planes occupied by the human body is in excess of a comfortable working temperature. A suitable position is within the angle of two walls or on an outside wall about 5 feet above floor-level, as indicated in Fig. 103.

Electric Cookers

Electric cookers cover a variety of types, from the small breakfast cooker to the heavy-duty cooking equipment suitable for canteens and hotels. The feminine interest in electric cooking has been dealt with elsewhere,* so this section will be confined to general examples and the electrical aspect.

The uniformity of the amount of heat provided from one

* Teach Yourself Books: "Household Electricity," Caroline Haslett.

FIG. 105.—Two-plate Cooker.   FIG. 106.—Modern Cooker.
(*General Electric Co. Ltd.*)

unit and the consistent results that can be obtained are one of the greatest advantages of the electric cooker, besides its general cleanliness and the absence of fumes and dirt.

A recent survey states that full-sized electric cookers are used by 85·7 per cent. of consumers, the remainder being of the " breakfast type," with or without oven. A simple two-plate cooker on legs is illustrated in Fig. 105. It has thermostatic oven control and simmer-switch on an 8-in. radiant boiling plate. A larger model is shown in Fig. 106. This has thermostatic oven control, a simmer-switch on the large boiling plate and three-heat switches on the small boiling plate and grill boiler. The oven door is of the " drop down " type and a warming drawer is provided in the base. An auto-timer can be fitted if desired and are suitable for A.C. supply only.

The desired oven temperature is obtained by setting the control dial at the requisite temperature, which is maintained within close limits, as shown by the graph in Fig. 107.

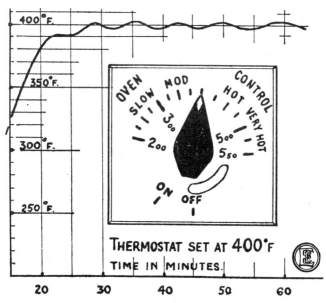

FIG. 107.—Temperature Control by Thermostat.

With automatic oven control the thermostat is of the bi-metallic type and is only suitable for A.C. supplies.

In the majority of cookers " plug-in " elements are pro-vided and the spaces between the oven walls are lined with heat-insulating material. Such additions as foot-pedals for door-opening and an interior glass door to view the interior without the risk of cooling draughts are provided on some models, and the oven can be arranged at different levels.

The performance and life of all boiling-plates are now greatly improved and the plates are rapid in action. There are two types of boiling-plate : The enclosed type which presents a smooth black surface from which the heat is transferred by conduction, and the radiant type, with a reflector-plate on the underside, in which the heat transfer is mainly by radiation, though the flattened element is in partial contact with the utensil.

With the former type, utensils having flat machined bottoms are desirable, whilst with the latter direct contact is not essential.

The element of the enclosed type is embedded in grooves underneath the cast-iron plate and retained in place by a special cement ; the cast-iron plate must be earthed. The radiant type consists of a nickel-chrome heating spiral enclosed in a steel tube and insulated therefrom by magnesium oxide. Such plates are more efficient and convenient than the former type but are somewhat more expensive, and some cookers are fitted with one or more of each type. The loading of an 8-inch boiling-plate is about 2000 watts, whilst the 6-inch size takes about 900 watts.

The grilling element is often in the form of an open wire spiral with a cast-iron plate above which can be used for cooking at the same time, and the loading is about 2000 watts, depending upon the size. Boiling-plates and grill elements are separately provided with three-heat control by means of bold rotary switches which connect the two sections of the element in parallel for " High," one section only for " Medium," and two sections in series for " Low " heat, the ratios of the heat obtained being 4 : 2 : 1.

Connection of Cookers

This should be carried out by a competent installation contractor or by the Supply Authority's employees if the cooker is on hire purchase. The cooker must be provided with a control unit with a double-pole main switch, so that the cooker can be completely disconnected from the supply.

A three-pin socket may be included for the electric kettle, though with some cookers this is fitted on the front panel of the cooker. A schematic diagram of a cooker-control unit is given in Fig. 108, whilst the interior view of such a switch is shown in Fig. 109, with a pilot lamp to indicate when the switch is on ; alternatively a visual indicator can be provided. The control switch may be of the change-over

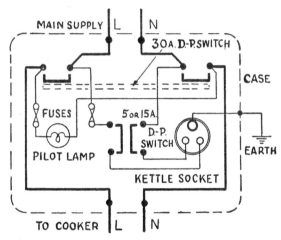

FIG. 108.—Cooker-control Unit with Pilot Lamp.

type, so that either the cooker or wash-boiler (alternatively the immersion heater) may be in circuit, as depicted in Fig. 110. The cooker has its own main and sub-circuit fuses (which should only be replaced by a competent person), so the control switch has only two single-pole fuses in the live side to protect the pilot lamp and the three-pin plug. The cooker is connected to the main switch of the supply by V.I.R. cable in conduit, which is often of the flexible type. The live main must be connected to the terminal on the cooker to which the switches are connected.

Earthing. It is essential that the cooker and its control

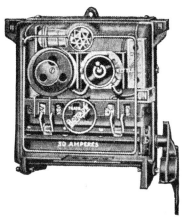

Fig. 109.—Cooker-control Switch, Interior View.
(*Bill Switchgear Ltd.*)

Fig. 110.—Control Switch with Change-over to Cooker or Boiler.
(*Bill Switchgear Ltd.*)

switch are properly earthed either through the conduit or by means of a separate earthing conductor.

Electric Kettles

An electric kettle is an essential adjunct to an electric cooker, as the use of a hotplate for boiling water is less efficient and takes up useful cooking-space. Electric kettles are of two types, one with an external heating element (which is obsolete) and the more efficient type with an internal immersion element. A safety device should be incorporated to ensure interruption of the supply if the kettle boils dry. Kettles should always be fitted with three-core cables and a three-pin plug, so that they are effectively earthed.

Electric Irons

It pays to buy a good-quality iron and numerous reliable makes are on the market. A well-balanced iron with a

handle so shaped that fatigue is minimised, together with
the correct shape and weight, should be chosen. The most
common source of trouble is with the flexible connection,

Fig. 111.—Electric Iron.
(*General Electric Co.*)

and a good-quality three-core flexible cable should be used.
In use, the iron must not be left flat on the table or it will
burn right through the wood, and some fires have been
caused by this happening. A 750-watt light-weight iron
with thermostatic control is illustrated in Fig. 111.

Electric Water Heaters

Even though many houses obtain hot water by means of
coal fires or slow-combustion boilers, the provision of
electric water heaters is an added convenience with high
inherent efficiency, automatic action, and freedom from
dirt and fumes.

There are four main types of electric water heaters :

(*a*) Storage heaters of the pressure or displacement type.

(*b*) Immersion heaters (including internal and external
circulators).

(*c*) Instantaneous heaters, or geysers.

(*d*) Electrode boilers.

A pressure type of storage heater should be used for new
construction or the conversion of an existing domestic
hot-water system, as a properly designed unit is more
efficient and cheapest in the long run.

Immersion heaters have been widely used, especially for

conversion jobs where first cost is of primary importance, but their efficiency is lower and they have often been added to the hot-water system as an afterthought.

Electric geysers give small quantities of hot water instantaneously. They have a very high electric loading, and thus are not viewed with favour by Supply Authorities due to the heavy intermittent loads. A small unit requires about 3 kW, whilst for a quick bath about 10 kW is required.

The electrode water heater is only applicable where large quantities of hot water are required for central heating or toilet purposes, and it is not used in normal-sized houses. The principle of operation depends upon the heating effect of a current passing through the water between a system of electrodes suitably arranged for the supply. These two latter types will not be considered in any greater detail.

Pressure-type Storage Heater

This type of storage heater obtains its pressure due to the head of water in the cistern, which is approximately $\frac{1}{2}$ lb. pressure per foot of head. The heater consists of an inner container of welded copper, tinned inside and out, with an outer casing of sheet steel, the intervening space being packed with granulated cork to provide heat insulation. The smaller sizes are suitable for wall mounting, whilst the larger capacities are provided with feet for floor mounting.

A modern type of automatic electric storage heater is shown in Fig. 112. The author is indebted to Messrs. Aidas Electric Ltd. for the following information. This apparatus has been designed to meet the demand in flats and small kitchens where space is restricted, and the dimensions are such that it can be accommodated in the space under the draining-board. This location is ideal because of the short length of pipe to the sink, where the largest and most frequent demand for hot water occurs. The two sizes, 15 and 20 gallon, are both of the same height and two

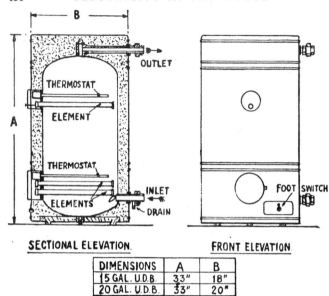

FIG. 112.—Pressure-type Electric Storage Heater.

(*Aidas Electric Ltd.*)

separate apparatus plates are provided. One near the top consists of one 500-watt element controlled by its own 5-amp. thermostat, whilst the bottom plate has four or five elements of 500 watts each for the respective sizes, controlled by a 15-amp. thermostat. The top element will provide a constant supply of hot water sufficient for washing-up and cleaning purposes, whilst the bottom element can be switched on when baths are required, by means of a foot-press switch incorporated at the bottom of the heater. All the 500-watt elements are interchangeable and withdrawable when the heater is full; the internal wiring is complete, so that the electrical fitting is confined to the necessary connections to a double-pole switch and the provision of a good earth connection.

The arrangement of this Sadia Type U.D.B. (under-draining-board) Water Heater for an independent service is shown in Fig. 113, in which the heater is directly fed from the ball-tank. When working in conjunction with an

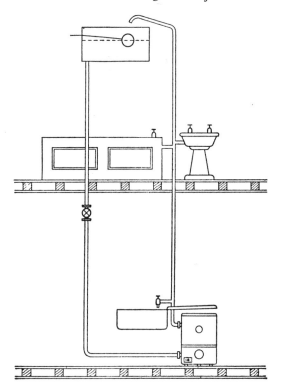

FIG. 113.—Pressure Water Heater for Independent Service.

(*Aidas Electric Ltd.,*

existing hot-water system the arrangement is shown in Fig. 114. It is fed by hot water from the boiler through the existing hot-water storage tank. This apparatus works at an all-round efficiency of 92 per cent., and it is estimated that, with electricity at 1d. per unit, ample hot water can be provided for a family of five for less than 6s. per week.

Another recent development is the use of a pressure-type heater to work in conjunction with a solid-fuel boiler in which the waste heat from the flue gases gives direct circula-

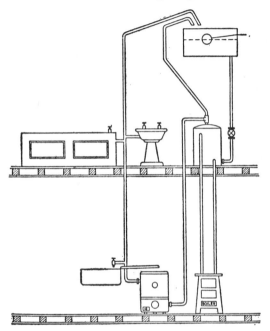

FIG. 114.—Pressure Water Heater in Conjunction with an Existing Hot-water System.

(*Aldas Electric Ltd.*)

tion with the electric water heater.   This interesting system is shown in Fig. 115,* from which the dual method of water-heating is apparent.

For normal domestic demands a pressure storage heater of 30 gallons capacity, with 2 kW loading, is the largest size

* Provisional Patent No. 6745/44.

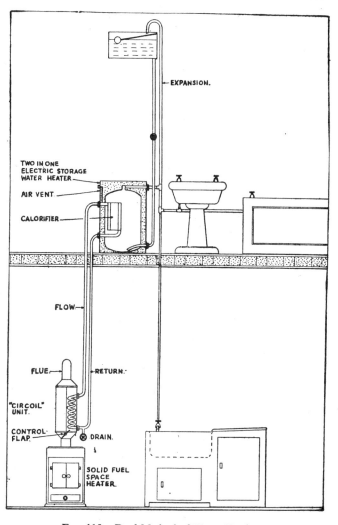

FIG. 115.—Dual Method of Water Heating.

(*Aldas Electric Ltd.*)

recommended; but when in doubt, advice should be obtained as to the most suitable size to install.

Free-outlet Types

Self-contained water heaters from $1\frac{1}{2}$ gallons capacity to supply one point are operated on the displacement principle

Fig. 116.—Free-outlet Water Heater.
(Aidas Electric Ltd.)

and *must be provided with a free outlet*, so that pressure cannot build up within the container. When the control tap is turned on, the entering cold water displaces an equivalent volume of hot water into the washhand-basin or sink. Thermostatic control is provided and the electrical and water connections are quite simple; for the 1½- and 3-gallon sizes (see Fig. 116) direct connection is made to the water-main, whilst the larger sizes are fed from a cistern.

It is essential before installing any type of water heater to see that it is suitable for the local water and that the water board's regulations are not infringed.

Immersion Heaters

There are several different arrangements of heating elements. The flat-bladed type is illustrated in Fig. 117,

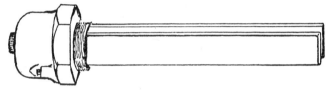

FIG. 117.—Two-blade Immersion Heater.

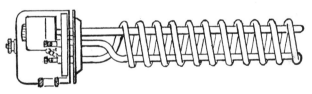

FIG. 118.—Spiral Immersion Heater.

(Aidas Electric Ltd.)

whilst a spiral-rod type, which is less liable to collect " fur " with hard water, is shown in Fig. 118.

The tubular immersion heater with three withdrawable elements and a thermostat mounted *above* is shown in Fig. 119 for an existing rectangular tank in an airing cupboard.

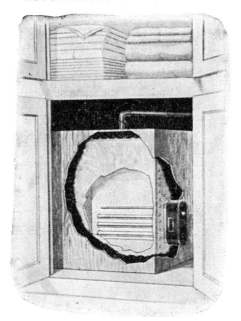

Fig. 119.—Tubular Immersion Heater installed in Airing Cupboard.

(Aidas Electric Ltd.)

Electric Circulators

This type of heater depends upon convection currents causing efficient circulation of the water. They have the advantage that should all the hot water be used, due to the rapid convection currents, a further smaller quantity of really hot water is quickly stored in the top of the tank. Figs. 120 and 121 illustrate side- and top-entry circulators.

Conversion of Existing Hot-water Systems

The success of the conversion depends upon the condition and layout of the existing pipe work. Secondary circulating radiators or hot-water taps joined to the boiler flow-pipe

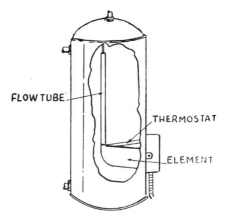

FIG. 120.—Side-entry Circulator.

(*Aidas Electric Ltd.*)

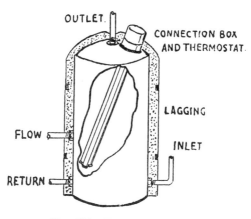

FIG. 121.—Top-entry Circulator.

(*Aidas Electric Ltd.*)

are not economically supplied. Expert advice should be obtained before an installation is commenced. In general the installation will be satisfactory where—

(1) The tank is efficiently lagged;

(2) The run of the hot-water pipes is short and not in exposed positions; and

(3) The hot-water pipes are all connected to the top of the tank or expansion pipe.

Settings for Thermostats

With soft water and up to about 12° hardness the thermostat may be set to interrupt the supply at a water temperature of 175° F.; with hardness varying from 12° to 20° the thermostat should not be set over 150° F. or the formation of scale will require frequent maintenance.

Water-heating Data

With water-heating we are able to calculate the power required with a greater degree of accuracy than with space-heating, and, as before, 1 kilowatt hour = 3412 B.Th.U. As 1 gallon of water weighs 10 lb., 1 unit of electricity will raise the temperature of 341 gallons of water by 1° F. This neglects the effect of losses. Allowing for these, the efficiency of heat conversion varies from about 92 per cent. with good lagging to less than 80 per cent. for unlagged tanks. Thus:

$$\text{Number of units (kWh)} = \frac{\text{Gallons} \times \text{temperature rise °F.}}{341 \times \text{efficiency}}$$

From this equation the size of heater required to heat a given quantity of water in a given time may be ascertained. Assuming for easy calculation an efficiency of 88 per cent., we obtain 300 in the denominator, then, either

$$\text{Size of heater in kW} = \frac{\text{Gallons} \times \text{temp. rise °F.}}{\text{Time in hours} \times 300} \quad \text{or}$$

$$\text{Gallons} = \frac{\text{kW} \times \text{time in hours} \times 300}{\text{Temp. rise °F.}}$$

Various Temperatures (Fahrenheit and Centigrade)

| | Degrees | |
	Fahrenheit	Centigrade
Boiling-water temperature	212	100
Scalding temperature	158	70
Washing-up dishes, temperature ..	122	50
Bath, average temperature	104	40

The average room temperature is 60° F., which is approximately 15° C.; whilst cold-water inlet temperatures may vary from 40° to 70° F., depending upon the locality and the season.

Approximate Capacity of Tanks

$$\text{Cylindrical tank} = \frac{(\text{Diameter})^2 \times \text{height}}{350} \text{ gallons}$$

$$\text{Rectangular tank} = \frac{\text{Length} \times \text{breadth} \times \text{height}}{280} \text{ gallons}$$

All the above tank dimensions are in inches. As a rough rule, 1 unit of electricity will boil 2 gallons of water starting from cold.

Example 16. A cylindrical tank is 12 in. diameter and 24 in. high. How many gallons will it hold and what size of immersion heater should be fitted if all the water is to be heated from 40° F. to 160° F. in 2 hours ?

$$\text{Cylindrical tank} = \frac{12^2 \times 24}{350} = 10 \text{ gallons.}$$

$$\text{Size of heater} = \frac{10 \times (160-40)}{2 \times 300} = 2 \text{ kW.}$$

CHAPTER VIII

LAYOUT OF THE INSTALLATION

The installation for two different houses is now described. The first one is a detached house in which no solid fuel or gas is used and electricity serves for all purposes. The second installation is for a small semi-detached house, and in this case the electrical installation is on a more modest scale, as solid fuel is used and the house was carcased for gas.

(1) Electrical Installation of a Detached House

The V.I.R. cables used are of the better quality made by a member-firm of the British Cable Makers' Association (C.M.A.) and are known as " 250-volt grade." The second quality, " 250-volt class," have the trade-name " Nonazo," and is used for jobs where the price is a consideration. Cheap foreign cables should not be used, as the saving on first cost is often lost in earlier replacements. For 400-volt 3-phase 4-wire supplies the same grade of cables can be used, as the phase-voltage to neutral is 230 volts. All cables are run in $\frac{5}{8}$- and $\frac{3}{4}$-inch screwed welded conduit with inspection fittings, care being taken to maintain continuity and a good earth connection.

Lighting Schedule

The lighting load is shown in the lighting schedule given in Fig. 122, which also shows the superficial area of the various rooms. The 5-amp. socket-outlets are considered with the lighting, but there is no need to differentiate between the different circuits except when there are separate tariffs for power and lighting. The sizes of socket-outlets have been confined to 5 and 15 amp. The electric-clock

LIGHTING SCHEDULE.

GROUND FLOOR.

Room.	Size	Area Sq. Ft.	Lighting Points.	Outlets. 5A. Sockets	Watts/Room General Lighting	Watts per Sq. Ft.
Dining Room.	17'·0"×11'·6"	196	3 - 60 w.	3	180	0·92
Music Room.	12'-3"×13'·6"	165	1 - 150w.	2	150	0·91
Study.	8'·6"×10·0"	86	1 - 100w.	2	100	1·16
Hall.	8'·0"×11·6"	92	1 - 60 w.	1	60	0·65
Lobby, Lavatory, W.C.			25, 40,15 w.		80	
Kitchen.	12·6"×8·0"	100	2 - 100 w. 2 - 15 w.←in cupboards.	1	200 30	2·0
Wash-house.	6'·0"×5·6"	33	1 - 40 w.		40	1·21
Tool-shed	6'·0"×4·0"	24	1 - 25 w.		25	1·04
Porches.	Front and Back		2 - 25 w		50	
Garage.	8'6"×15·0"	127	1- 100w. 1 - 40 w.	1 Bench.	140	
			Ground Floor.	10	1055 w.	
FIRST FLOOR.						
Bedroom No 1.	17'·0"×11'·6"	196	60, 40, 25 w.	1	125	0·64
,, No 2.	12·6"×14·0"	175	60, 40, 25 w.	1	125	0·71
,, No 3.	12·6"×8·4½	104	60, 25 w.	1	85	0·82
Sewing-room.	8'·0"×10·0"	80	1 - 100w.	1	100	1·25
Bath-room.	8·4½×7·0"	59	1 - 100w.	None.	100	1·70
W.C.			1 - 25 w.		25	
Top of stairs & Landing			60, 25 w	1	85	
Airing-cupboard.			1 - 15 w.		15	
			First Floor.	5	660 w	
			TOTAL.	15	1·715 kW	

FIG. 122.—Details of Room Sizes and Lighting Outlets.

points and the bell transformer take only a small current, so they have not been included.   The positions of switches and various outlets are indicated by British Standard symbols in the plan (Fig. 123), but the conduit runs are not

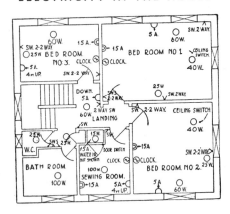

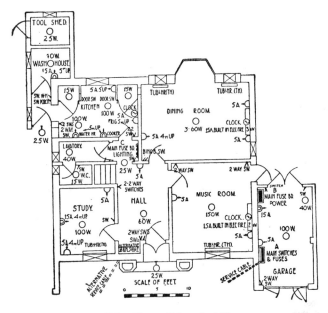

FIG. 123.—Plans of Detached House.

Photo: General Electric Co. Ltd.

PLATE 3. Fully automatic washing machine which will wash, rinse and spin dry with a selection of water temperatures and wash times

PLATE 4. Refrigerator with freezer compartment for frozen food, salad, bin, egg and milk racks, etc.

included. It is advisable to arrange the larger rooms so that they are not dependent on one sub-circuit, also different poles or phases must not be brought in so that there is any possibility of connection across the live conductors.

The Supply Authority's fuses and meter are shown in the garage at A, mounted at a reasonable height on the wall and adjacent to the incoming service cable. All this gear should be iron-clad. The consumer's main switches and fuses, or splitter, can either be at A or, if desired, at B, adjacent to the rear door of the garage. An alternative point of entry is shown to the left of the front door, with the distribution fuse-boards at C at the back of the hall. The final choice of these positions depends upon the local requirements.

Estimation of Current

The total general lighting is 1715 watts, which with a 230-volt supply gives a current of 7·5 amp., though this will never be on at one time, and the sizes of some of the lamps may be altered to suit individual requirements. The 5-amp. socket outlets on the lighting circuit must all be taken at their full value when fixing the size of cable, even though they may not be loaded to capacity. Where 2-amp. outlets are used, they are looped-out from the lighting circuit; but in this layout the socket-outlets are kept to 5 amp. for lighter loads and 15 amp. for the heavier currents. called power.

Considering the ground floor, the maximum lighting load is 1055 watts, which requires 4·6 amp. at 230 volts. As there are nineteen lamps, at least two ways must be run from the distribution board, with 3/·029 cables. There are ten 5-amp. socket-outlets, which when wired with 3/·029 must have a circuit each running back to the fuse-board ; thus a minimum of twelve ways are required.

On the first floor the maximum lamp load is 660 watts, which requires 2·9 amp. at 230 volts. There are fourteen lamps, so two ways are required, together with five for the

5-amp. socket outlets; thus a minimum of seven ways are needed. A total of twenty ways should be provided, leaving one " spare." With the above arrangement of 5-amp. outlets all the sub-circuit fuses would be for 5 amp., though another arrangement is illustrated in the second installation. Standard 15-amp. fuse-carriers should be used for all circuits, both for power and lighting.

Details of Switching and Outlets

The dining-room is shown with a central fitting for general lighting, containing three 60-watt lamps, controlled by two switches. A " Binob " switch gives a compact arrangement for one, two, or three lights, or a flush mounting with two separate switches can be used. The switch is mounted near the door, at the same side as the handle, 4 feet to 4 feet 6 inches above the floor. This common height should be maintained throughout the house, except in children's rooms, where 6 feet is more desirable, though this height is not a real deterrent to playing with the lights. A 5-amp. socket is provided on each side of the built-in electric fire, towards the top of the skirting-board, to give an alternative socket for a standard lamp or radio set ; the latter should be connected by means of a 2-amp. fused plug. The 5-amp. socket-outlet on the opposite wall is placed 4 feet to 4 feet 6 inches above the floor to supply a plate-warmer for the sideboard or additional lighting. A permanent fixed clock-point is provided above the fire-place ; this obviates trailing leads to the synchronous clock and is also indicated in other rooms.

The music-room has a 150-watt central fitting with two-way switching adjacent to each door. Two 5-amp. socket-outlets are provided for additional portable lamps, the arrangement of which depends upon the position of the piano.

The study is provided with a 100-watt central fitting ; but if the walls are at all dark or there are many book-shelves. a greater power would be needed. The two 5-amp. outlets allow for portable or desk lighting. The positions of these various outlets depend upon the wishes of the occupier and the distribution of the furniture, as no bracket lighting has been indicated. The 5-amp. sockets are useful for the vacuum cleaner and are provided for that purpose in the ground-floor hall and first-floor landing. The author's preference is for interlocking switches, so that the plug cannot be withdrawn when the circuit is " live " or be switched " on " when the plug is out ; but the socket-outlets with protecting shutters and no switches are quite popular and give good protection.

The kitchen has two 100-watt lamps in enclosed fittings, which, it is suggested, should be arranged diagonally to give good illumination to the cooker and sink on one side and the work-table between the larder and a cupboard which gives access to the serving-hatch. In each of these cupboards a 15-watt lamp is mounted in a ceiling fitting, controlled by door-switches which go " on " when the doors are opened. A similar arrangement is fitted to the airing-cupboard on the first floor. The main lighting is controlled by two two-way switches at each door.

The wash-house has an enclosed fitting, the switch being outside the door, adjacent to that for the porch-light, which is an enclosed bracket fitting.

The hall and first-floor landing are provided with 60-watt lamps, both with two-way switching.

The garage is dealt with later on.

The bedrooms are provided with a 60-watt lamp in front of the dressing-table, and a 25-watt pendent lamp over the bed, or alternatively a portable bedside lamp can be provided from a 5-amp. socket-outlet mounted 4 feet up the wall. In the first and second bedrooms a 40-watt lamp is arranged in front of the wardrobe. The switches are shown near the door, on the same side as the handle, and two-way switching is provided from the bed and door positions. Ceiling-switches can be used for the wardrobe light and bed-switch.

The bathroom is provided with a 100-watt enclosed fitting and the switch is outside the door. If the occupier insists on an inside switch, the ceiling type should be used. This amount of lighting may appear excessive, but with an enclosed fitting a good light for shaving is a great convenience.

The illumination of the sewing-room should be generous, hence a 100-watt lamp is used with a 5-amp. socket-outlet to provide another portable lamp or supply the sewing machine if an electric model is used.

The other lighting arrangements do not call for any special comments and the sizes of lamps given are a minimum. The power circuits for heavier currents will be dealt with in the next section.

Power Schedule

The 15-amp. socket-outlets, electric fires, and other apparatus taking larger currents, are given in the Power Schedule on p. 153, and the various outlets are indicated on the plan (Fig. 123). There are ten outlets requiring 15-amp. wiring, 7/·029-inch cables, of which seven are of the three-pin type with interlocking switch, two are electric fires, and one goes to the water heater.

In the dining-room a 3-kW built-in fire is fitted, whilst in the music-room a 2-kW fire is sufficient. The 15-amp. socket-outlet in the study is of the flush pattern mounted 4 feet up the wall and can be used either for a 2-kW portable fire or panel heating if desired, In the three main ground-floor rooms tubular heaters are fitted under the windows, each consisting of a bank of two tubes 4 feet long taking 480 watts, which on a 230-volt supply requires 2 amp., so 3/·029 cable is large enough. Thermostats are mounted in the corners of the rooms on the outer walls so as to switch off these heaters when the room temperature exceeds 60° F. When the other electric radiant heating is not in use, these tubular heaters serve to keep the rooms aired in cold weather. A similar arrangement of convector heaters

E.H.—G

are suitable for the bedrooms, but have not been included as a 15-amp. socket-outlet is provided. One method of warming the bathroom is by a panel heater fitted near the ceiling and efficiently earthed. An electric towel-rail 2 feet 6 inches long and loaded at 75 watts is provided. Larger sizes and water-filled towel-rails are also available.

The kitchen contains the cooker, the control unit of which is supplied from a separate 30-amp. main switch. A pair of 7/·044 cables will carry 30 amp., but 7/·052 is often specified. The 20-gallon water heater, rated at 1500

POWER SCHEDULE FOR DETACHED HOUSE

Room	15-amp. Outlets	Heaters	Other Apparatus	—
Dining-room	1 3-kW fire	2 tubular, 960 W.		
Music-room	1 2-kW fire	1 tubular 480 W.		
Study	1 15-A socket	1 tubular, 480 W.		
Kitchen	..	..	Cooker, 30-A Water heater 1500 W.	Alternative, 500 W.
Wash-house	1 15-A socket			
Garage	1 15-A socket			
Bedroom No. 1	1 15-A socket			
Bedroom No. 2	1 15-A socket			
Bedroom No. 3	1 15-A socket			
Sewing-room	1 15-A socket			
Bathroom	..	1 panel, 750 W.	Water heater	Alternative, 1500 W.

W., takes 6·5 amp., but this socket-outlet is wired with 7/·029 similar to the other 15-amp. socket-outlets.

If extra heating is required in the kitchen for cold mornings, the 5-amp. socket-outlet at the side of the work-table is large enough for a portable 1-kW fire.   The refrigerator is connected to a 5-amp. fused plug, as the running current is well below this value, and this can be looped off a convenient circuit.   If the alternative arrangement of a 5-gallon water heater, rated at 500 watts, for the sink and adjacent lavatory is substituted, then the 1500-watt water heater will be floor-mounted in the linen-cupboard and connected to another phase to equalise the loading.   This water heater could also supply fitted basins in the two larger bedrooms, as well as the bath, and should then be at least 2000 watts.   With the original arrangement a small tubular heater would be required in the linen-cupboard.

The wash-house is provided with an ironclad 15-amp. socket-outlet mounted 5 feet up the wall.   This size is large enough for a wash-boiler, and 7/·029 cables are desirable for an electric washer with a single-phase motor.

Estimation of Current

All this load will not be on at once, and various diversity factors have been proposed for different types of load.   We will make an estimate based on the total power-load, as even though considerable lighting has been tabulated it is only a small addition to the power-load.

" Power " current :

7 15-amp. socket-outlets 105 A. taking one-third ..	35 amp.
Electric fires, taking 3 kW	13 „
Water heater, 2 kW maximum, taking 1·5 kW	7 „
Tubular and panel heaters, 11 A., taking 8 A. ..	8 „
Cooker, 30 A.	30 „
	93 „

With a 3-phase 4-wire supply this is 31 amp. per phase. This estimated current is the same as taking a total load of 175 amp., and allowing the first 10 amp., plus half the remainder, i.e. $10 + \frac{165}{2} = 93$ amp.

Main Supply

For this load one phase may be insufficient ; either two phases would be brought in, depending upon the load on the road, or perhaps a 3-phase 4-wire A.C. supply would be given.   One method of arranging this is shown in Fig. 124, in which a three-phase splitter with neutral bus-bar splits up each phase into two fused ways which go to 30-amp. main switches for " power " and 15-amp. main switches for

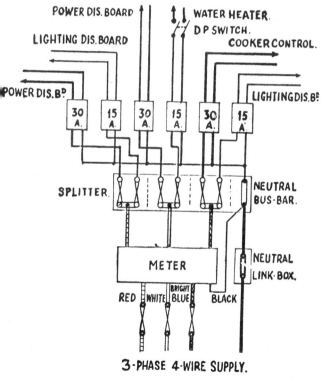

FIG. 124.—Main Supply Fuses and Switches.

H*

" lighting " circuits. The cables from these switches go to the distribution boards for the various sub-circuits, An alternative method is to use six switch fuses.

If a single main switch fuse is used which switches in the neutral, instead of using a solid neutral link, the neutral switch blade is made to " make " first and " break " last.

Often inadequate facilities are provided for the use of electrical apparatus. In houses of the future the former scarcity of outlets must not occur, though the next layout is more modest for a smaller house.

(2) Installation of Small Semi-detached House

The two floor-plans of this house are shown in Fig. 125. Enough outlets are indicated by standard symbols, but the lighting is confined to single points. The power is limited to a 1-kW electric fire, two portable fires of this size being sufficient, as coal fires are available in four rooms. There is a coke-boiler in the kitchen which also warms the bedroom above by the hot-water pipes to the tank in the linen-cupboard. Five-ampere socket-outlets with interlocking switches may be provided. This leads to economy in wiring, as it is permissible to connect two 5-amp. outlets to one cable run from the distribution board. The additional 2-amp. socket-outlets are confined to lighting and small-current apparatus, such as a radio set. Three pin-plugs are fitted, the live sockets being protected by shutters to prevent accidental contact with the live portions. These 2-amp. socket-outlets are all mounted at a height of 4 feet 6 inches, the same as the switches, which should be of the sunk type. This mounting height is about the height of the mantelpieces in the ground-floor rooms, and such a height is more convenient for switching off when in bed instead of reaching down to the skirting-board.

Two main cable runs for lighting are laid, one up to the loft dropping down to the bedrooms, whilst the other goes to the space below the first floor to drop down to the ground-floor fittings.

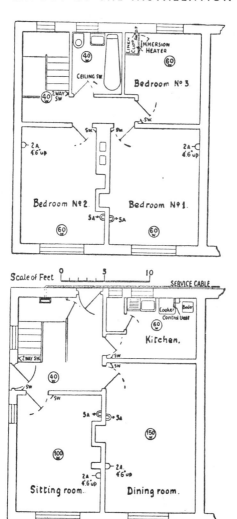

FIG. 125.—Layout of Semi-detached House.

The incoming supply runs along the back of the houses, the service cable entering beneath the stairs.

The lighting schedule is given below, from which it will be seen that the connected lighting load is 740 watts. The supply is 210 volt (A.C.), which gives a maximum current of 3·5 amp., which is not demanded in practice.

LIGHTING SCHEDULE

Room	Size	Area sq. ft.	Watts at 0·75W./sq. ft.	2-amp. Sockets	Lamp size Watts
	ft. in. ft. in.				
Dining-room	16 0 × 10 6	160	120		150
				1	40
Sitting-room	12 6 × 9 3	116	87		100
				1	40
Kitchen ..	10 0 × 6 6	65	48	..	60
Hall ..	..	63	47	..	40
			Ground-floor total		430
Bedroom No.1	12 6 × 10 0	125	94		60
				1	25
Bedroom No. 2	12 6 × 9 3	116	87		60
				1	25
Bedroom No. 3	10 0 × 8 6	85	64	..	60
Bathroom and W.C. ..	..	..	..	..	40
Stairs and top landing ..	..	..	..	..	40
			First-floor total		310

Small Semi-detached House.   Total lighting load   ..   ..   740W.

Total Current

The maximum power load is 20 amp. The cooker is rated at 20 amp. (4 kW) and the 2-kW immersion heater can be called 10 amp. Thus the total connected load is 53·5 amp.

Taking the first ten amperes of connected load and one-half of the remainder gives a current of 32 amp., so 7/·044 inch (0·01 sq. inch) is large enough for the main cable.

The cooker takes the heaviest load and requires 7/·036 inch, and the separate circuit for the immersion heater should be run in 7/·029 inch. Both these circuits should be in conduit. The remainder of the wiring can be in conduit for a first-class job, but most likely T.R.C. would be used.

The power-plugs would consist of two runs of 3/·036 inch, with two 5-amp. socket-outlets connected to each run ; whilst the lighting cables would be 3/·029 inch. In a small house like this with short runs there is no need to worry about voltage-drop calculations.

With an " all-in tariff " the distribution board requires four ways fitted with standard 15-amp. fuse-holders, two of which would be fused at 10 amp. for the power sockets and two fused at 5 amp. for the lighting circuits. This does not permit of any extensions, which, if provided for, need a six-way board.

The cooker and immersion heater have separate circuits, but with some authorities the cooker and immersion heater (or wash-boiler) are connected to a change-over switch, so that the immersion heater cannot be on at the same time as the cooker and vice versa. The immersion heater would have thermostatic control and a separate switch in the airing cupboard. This layout gives enough outlets for minimum convenience.

Future Development of Domestic Installations

The period of building during the inter-war period saw the general adoption of the conduit system, and both T.R.S. and lead-covered cables were developed in various wiring systems, but the electrical installation was still *added* to the conventional methods of construction and often no regard was given to the material employed and the convenience to the user of the completed installation.

Future developments must aim at providing *service* for the prospective occupier of modern dwellings which will fulfil all reasonable requirements for the essential utilities,

H*

including electricity, so that safety, adequacy, and availability are a feature throughout the house, which should be designed and built as a single entity.

Various proposals have appeared in the technical press, and in the *Journal of the Institution of Electrical Engineers*, Vol. 90, Part II, No. 18, of December 1943, an excellent paper entitled " The Future of Domestic Wiring Installations " by Forbes Jackson, W. J. H. Wood, G. Smith, and E. Jacobi deals with (i) immediate developments, and (ii) the distant view. The reader is referred to this paper and the accompanying discussions for much interesting information in greater detail than can be given here. In the second portion of the paper a more liberal use of electricity is envisaged, with the actual load to be taken by domestic premises proportioned to room volume of 1·5 watts per cubic foot, whilst if only lighting is considered 3 watts per square foot is suggested. If such figures are adopted, then there must be provision for many more socket-outlets than in the past, and to make this possible a ring-main system with single-pole fusing is proposed.

A ring-main consists of a loop of two active conductors which goes round a room or floor and to which a number of socket-outlets can be connected without cutting the cables. Such a ring-main is generally shown by a single-line diagram, even though it is made up of two or three conductors, in the latter case " line," " neutral." and " earth." When the two ends of the ring are joined, as in Fig. 126 (*a*), the current can get round either way to the connected loads and the voltage drop is a minimum. If a break occurs in the ring at Y, then the 5-amp. load is supplied clockwise, whilst the other loads are supplied anti-clockwise. If the ring is not completed to the supply, it is like a distributor fed at one end (see Fig. 126 (*b*)), then with a break at Y only the 5-amp. load will be supplied.

If each load (i.e. socket-outlet) is provided with a separate fuse, in the event of an overload blowing the fuse on any one socket-outlet, only that load is affected and the ring-main will continue to supply current to the other loads. It is proposed that the ring-main be connected to the supply by a single fuse, in the line conductor, to protect the whole ring, the neutral wire not to be fused but to be solidly connected at the intake unit. A ring-main with general utility sockets and lighting together with the cooker circuit is shown for the ground floor of a small dwelling-house in Fig. 127.

The Kitchen

The kitchen is the wife's workshop and many different labour-saving devices will be required together with an adequate supply of hot water, an electric cooker, refrigerator, electric washer, electric clock with timing device, and radio.

These are some of the items now available, with the possibility of many more in the future. The layout of the kitchen should be such that it is planned to give the most complete service as a single entity. This cannot be achieved with only one or two outlet points fitted at positions which are assumed to be suitable. An ideal arrangement would be one every 2 to 3 feet around the kitchen, and this idea is not beyond the realms of possibility.

The provision of complete kitchen units which can be assembled on site is visualised, and some models have already been made, but large-scale production is not possible under present conditions. It is proposed that the bathroom should back on to the kitchen, so that the plumbing arrangements can also be prefabricated.

The apparatus must be co-ordinated under the following headings :

1. Basic requirement of apparatus, e.g. water, electricity.

2. Objective visibility under natural and artificial lighting.

3. Safety and convenience with the minimum fatigue in use.

4. Capability of rearrangement under change of family conditions and improvement in design.

One such arrangement of kitchen equipment is shown in

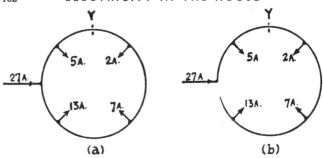

FIG. 126.—Ring-main with Four Socket-outlets.

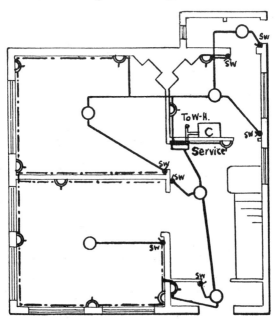

—— Conduit above Ceiling. ══ Conduit to Cooker.
— - — Conduit chased in wall at socket height.

FIG. 127.—Ring-main with General Utility Sockets.

Fig. 128, which is taken from the paper quoted earlier. With the use of new materials and installation methods, together with regulations which consider both convenience and sufficiency, as well as good technique and safety based on a recognised code of practice, much of the drudgery of housework can be removed at a cost which is not prohibitive.

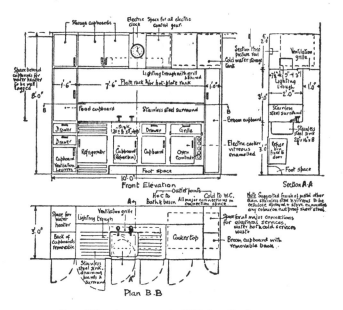

FIG. 128.—Arrangement of Kitchen Equipment.

(*J.I.E.E., Vol. 90, Part II, No. 18.*)

Socket-outlets

There are at present several different sizes of sockets, the earlier types with two pins (which do not give the safety of an earth connection), some with three round pins, whilst others have flat pins. It would greatly simplify matters, both during installation and in service, if all the socket-outlets on domestic premises were of the same size. The 15-amp. plug now used for power is often too large for its work, and the necessity of running 15-amp. cable is seldom justified in a small house, from the point of view of the current to be carried. It has been suggested that a universal 10-amp. socket with a fused plug would meet most needs in conjunction with a ring-main and single-pole fusing. There is no existing standard 10-amp. socket-outlet, even though some 5-amp. plugs of high-class nanufacture will stand 10 amp. To accept this size is only to perpetuate the existing confusion and annoyance, when any loads over 2 kW are to be connected to the mains.

One solution is to adopt 3 kW as the highest loading, which with the standard voltage of 230 gives 13 amp., and to provide suitable terminals for 7/·029-inch cable (15 amp.) as well as smaller wiring. With new installations such a procedure is rational, whilst the idea of fitting up-rated socket-outlets to old installations is in many cases dangerous, as the original cables are often too small for the increased current, which may lead to overheating and the risk of fires. The I.E.E. Wiring Rules prohibit fuses in sockets, and their addition entails increased socket size with the possibility of overheating and additional voltage drop.

Domestic Fused Plugs and Sockets

The author is indebted for the following informtaion to Messrs. Dorman & Smith Ltd., who have developed these essential items of domestic electrification. The earlier type is of the round pin pattern, the fused plug being easily removed for fuse renewal. They are suitable for loads up to 3 kW over the voltage range of 200 to 250. The size of plug is only slightly larger than the 2-amp. B.S. 546 plug and is smaller than the 5- and 15-amp. sizes to that specification as shown in Fig. 129.

These socket-outlets are suitable for ring main circuits and will fit a B.S. round conduit box and are fully shuttered and earthed. They provide an all-purpose plug for various appliances from a lamp standard to a 3-kW load which is 13 amp. at 230 volts.   Spare fused pins are rated at 3, 5, 7, 13 and 15 amp. and are colour coded.   All pins are solid with the terminals and may be pushed out for easy wiring as shown in Fig. 130.

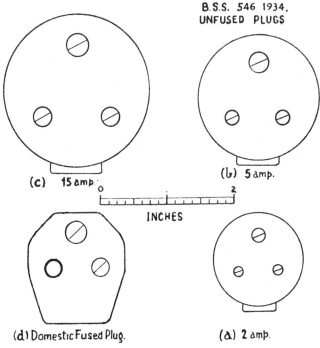

FIG. 129.—Relative Sizes of Plugs.

The plug with fuse removed is shown in Fig. 131.   The fuse is easily renewed away from live conductors and without the use of any tools.   The high-rupturing capacity fuses open the circuit without a report and a barely visible flash on short circuit and have been adequately tested by a competent authority.

FIG. 130.—Plug with Cap removed to show easy Wiring.
(*Dorman & Smith Ltd.*)

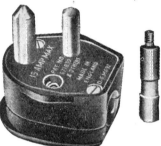

FIG. 131.—Domestic Plug with Fused Pin withdrawn.
(*Dorman & Smith Ltd.*)

FIG. 132.—Back of Domestic Socket Outlet.
(*Dorman & Smith Ltd.*)

The Socket and Wiring (Round Pin Plugs)

The socket-outlet is designed to fit a standard box and the back view is shown in Fig. 132.

This is so arranged that by baring a short length of the ring main conductors they may be connected without cutting or doubling back. The terminals will take three separate 7/·029 or a ring main of 7/·052 in. These circular shuttered socket outlets can be unswitched or switched. Alternatively a square shape in single-, twin or ganged arrangement are available for flush or surface mounting.

Rectangular Pin Fused Plugs and Shuttered Socket-outlet

A ring circuit and spurs (if any) in a house or flat may supply an unlimited number of 13-amp. socket-outlets, on the basis of one ring circuit for every 1000 sq. ft. of floor area or part thereof, providing the socket-outlets are reasonably distributed among the ring circuits when these are more than one. In one room of less than 200 sq. ft. floor area, which is not a kitchen, 3 socket-outlets are allowed but electric clocks fed through fused clock connectors are not included. The size of cable to be looped in is 7/·029 in. for the final sub-circuits. This means that each socket does not have to have a separate run back to the distribution board as all apparatus is protected by a cartridge fuse which should be of an appropriate rating in the plug connected to the appliance. In practice 13-amp. fuses are fitted in the plugs but it would be better if these were omitted and one of a suitable current rating supplied to suit the connected apparatus. This more rational system of wiring has grown in recent years and it is now common practice to install flat-pin plugs, on A.C. circuits only, instead of the earlier round-pin plugs which were common on both D.C. and A.C. supplies.* The rectangular pins of a fused plug can be seen in Fig. 133(a) in which a hinged pin is depressed to show the cartridge fuse which is easily re-

* A D.C. socket must be controlled by an adjacent switch, but for A.C. a readily withdrawable plug is allowed.

placed in a few seconds and is shown locked in position ready for insertion in Fig. 133(*b*).

FIG. 133 (*a*).—Flat-pin Fused Plug ready for Fuse withdrawal.
(*Dorman & Smith Ltd.*)

FIG. 133 (*b*).—Flat-pin Fused Plug ready for insertion in Socket-outlet.
(*Dorman & Smith Ltd.*)

Removable contact pins ensure easy and safe wiring and Fig. 134 illustrates this feature.

Flush and surface mounting units are available in single and multiple units without and with switches. If desired, a neon indicator light is provided with the switched sockets, as shown in Fig. 135.

FIG. 134.—Plug with Cap removed showing Method of Wiring.
(*Dorman & Smith Ltd.*)

FIG. 135.—Switched shuttered Socket-outlet with Neon Indicator light.
(*Dorman & Smith Ltd.*)

Miniature Circuit Breakers

These are now coming into use to replace fuses in the better domestic installations. The main switch is combined on a panel with four or six ways for the outgoing circuits, each of which is controlled by a miniature circuit breaker instead of a fuse. The advantages are elimination of fuse re-wiring or replacement, a visual indication of the blown circuit and the " free handle " action prevents closing the circuit if the fault persists. The units are rated at 30 amp., suitable for a cooker, 15 amp. for power outlets and 5 amp. for lighting circuits. The circuit breakers are sealed for safety so are immune from interference such as can occur when fuse links are fitted with any odd bit of wire to carry the current. These miniature circuit breakers have been tested on 250 volts A.C. to 3000 amp. and give good protection and discrimination by thermal operation on overload and a magnetic trip under heavy fault conditions. Such a breaker is shown in Fig. 136.

FIG. 136.—Miniature Circuit Breaker.

(Dorman & Smith Ltd.)

CHAPTER IX

TRANSFORMERS AND ELECTRIC MOTORS

Transformers are used on alternating-current supplies to obtain changes of voltage and current with the same amount of power. A transformer is a static piece of apparatus consisting of a laminated iron core on which is wound either two separate windings, i.e. a double-wound transformer, or a single coil with a tapping-point brought out, i.e. an auto-transformer as already illustrated in Fig. 97 Chapter VI.

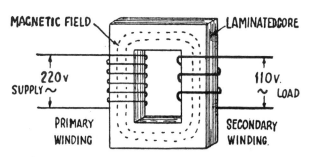

FIG. 137.—Diagram of a Transformer.

A transformer is represented in Fig. 137, with an alternating current supply of 220 volts applied to the left-hand coil, called the primary. An alternating magnetic field is set up in the iron core which induces an alternating e.m.f. in the right-hand coil, called the secondary. With half as many secondary turns as on the primary winding, 110 volts will be obtained across the secondary terminals. If this winding is connected to a load, a current is provided which is balanced by a primary current of practically half the secondary value. Transformers have very small losses, the voltage is proportional to the number of turns of *one* winding, whilst the current is inversely proportional to the turns ratio.

Transformers with iron cores are used for power applications, also low audio-frequencies in radio sets; at high radio-frequencies the iron core is omitted. Small transformers are mounted in either an iron or bakelite case and should be earthed. They are only suitable for alternating currents, and if connected to a direct-current supply of the same voltage they will get very hot and blow the fuses or else burn out.

Electric Motors

For domestic applications electric motors are of a small size and are known as fractional horse-power motors.

These small machines can be switched directly on to the supply, but must be suitably wound for the type of supply and declared voltage. Direct-current motors will not operate on an alternating current, and vice versa.

There is one type, called the Universal Motor, which will run on either D.C. or A.C. of a similar voltage. Such motors do not exceed $\frac{1}{4}$ h.p. and the majority of domestic motors are below this output.

Principle of the Electric Motor

An electric motor is used to convert electrical energy into a mechanical form and thus perform work at a certain rate. When a conductor is carrying an electric current it exhibits magnetic properties. If another magnet system is adjacent to this conductor there will be a mutual reaction and the wire will be forced in a certain direction. By a suitable arrangement of an iron electro-magnet portion, which is generally stationary, and another rotating portion called the armature, which carries a suitable winding, mechanical power is obtained.

Protection of Small Motors

The greater the output or horse-power of a motor, the more current it will take from the supply. If more work is demanded, the motor will take a greater current; if the overload is excessive, heat is generated and the speed of the motor will fall. To protect the motor, fuses a thermal device or a small circuit breaker is employed which opens the circuit when the current becomes excessive or an overload

Fig. 138.—Double-pole Circuit Breaker.
(*Nalder Bros. & Thompson Ltd.*)

persists for an appreciable time. A small double-pole circuit breaker which gives automatic protection to fractional horse-power motors is illustrated in Fig. 138. Such circuit breakers can also replace fuses on lighting and power circuits and with the calibrated setting give protection which cannot be modified by unauthorised persons. The total enclosure gives protection from injury and the " free handle " mechanism prevents the circuit breaker being closed on a fault, when used in place of a main switch-fuse.

Types of D.C. Motors

Even though D.C. motors are not now so common with the growth of A.C. supplies, their type-names and characteristics are given as they are often quoted. There are three types of D.C. motors: (i) Shunt, (ii) Series, and (iii) Compound, depending upon the arrangement of the field-magnet windings. The shunt motor runs at practically constant speed and its high-resistance field winding is connected in parallel with the armature.

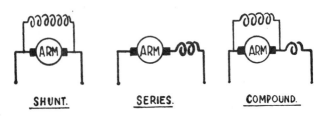

SHUNT.   SERIES.   COMPOUND.

Fig. 139.—Connections of D.C. Motors.

The series motor has low-resistance field-coils connected in series with the armature. The speed varies with the load, increasing as the latter falls, but it will exert a much greater turning moment, or torque, than the shunt motor at starting and low speeds.

The compound motor is a compromise between these two types and is used when the load demands a higher starting-torque than the shunt motor without the wide speed-variation of a series motor. One application is driving the compressor of a refrigerator.

The connections of these motors are given in Fig. 139, whilst Fig. 140 gives characteristic curves of speed and torque against current.

With D.C. motors there is complete electrical continuity between the terminals. The armature winding is fed from the commutator made up of copper segments insulated

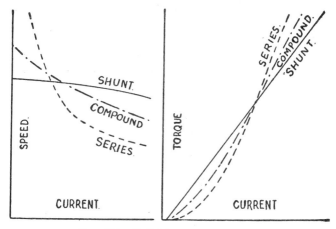

Fig. 140.—D.C. Motor Characteristics.

from one another, on which bear carbon brushes which form sliding contacts.

Wear of the brushes, dirty commutator, and poor connections are the usual sources of trouble in small motors.

Universal Motors

These motors can be used on either D.C. or A.C. supplies of the same voltage. The entire magnetic system is laminated and the speed varies with load, as is usual with series motors. The performance is not so good on A.C. as D.C., but it is quite suitable for vacuum cleaners, small fans, hair dryers, floor polishers, stirring machines, and other applications where the high speed is allowable. The armature is like a D.C. machine, but the brushes often require more frequent renewal.

Types of A.C. Motors

The A.C. series motor is similar to the Universal Motor and is the only common type in which the armature gets its current by conduction.

The basic principle of the static transformer is mutual induction between the windings, and this same principle applies to the induction motor, which can operate on three-, two-, or single-phase supplies. Even though small three-phase induction motors have been developed, the single-phase induction motor, either of the split-phase starting or of the shaded-pole type, is used for domestic applications, as only a single-phase supply is generally available. The single-phase motor is not inherently self-starting, but will continue to run once it is started. In the split-phase type an auxiliary winding temporarily makes the motor " two-phase " during the starting period, whilst in the shaded-pole motor a copper shading ring around half the pole gives the necessary starting torque.

Split-phase motors are suitable for applications where heavy starting-torques and overloads do not occur, e.g. electric washing machines fitted with a clutch. Shaded-pole motors are used for small slow-speed fans and electric clocks. These motors have a " shunt characteristic," i.e. the speed is nearly constant, but to improve the starting performance and overload capacity, two modifications have been made.

The Repulsion-start Induction-run Motor

This has one winding connected to the supply on the outer stationary portion, called the " stator," with an armature like a D.C. motor, but the brushes are connected together. It starts as a repulsion motor with a " series characteristic," and when it has run up to some 75 per cent. of full speed the armature winding is short-circuited and sometimes the brushes are lifted. It then runs as an induction motor.

The Capacitor Motor

The capacitor-start induction-run motor has two windings on the stator, one of which is connected to a condenser or capacitor, which in effect makes it a two-phase motor for starting. The auxiliary winding and condenser are cut out at a predetermined speed and the motor runs as an induction motor. An improved pattern is "Capacitor Start and Run," in which the condensers are regrouped after running up to speed and the performance is enhanced. The rotating armature is called the "rotor" and is of the robust squirrel-cage type; there is no electrical connection between the stator and rotor in either type. Although primarily developed for refrigerators and oil-burners, these motors are extremely well suited to other duties requiring operation for long periods, where maximum general efficiency is essential.

FIG. 141.—Capacitor Motor with Resilient Mounting.
(*British Thomson-Houston Co. Ltd.*)

A capacitor-start motor manufactured by the British Thomson-Houston Co., Ltd., is illustrated in Fig. 141. This motor has a resilient mounting. The robust rotor construction is evident from Fig. 142.

FIG. 142.—Rotor of Capacitor Motor.
(*British Thomson-Houston Co. Ltd.*)

In the author's opinion this is the most satisfactory type of single-phase F.H.P. motor, even though it is slightly more expensive in first cost than the ordinary split-phase motor. The relatively high efficiency and power factor is indicated in Fig. 143 together with the torque. Capacitor motors are inherently quiet, free from radio interference, and economical in running cost which more than saves the original capital outlay.

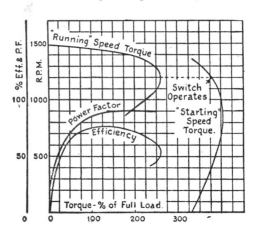

FIG. 143.—Capacitor-motor Characteristics.

(*British Thomson-Houston Co. Ltd.*)

Synchronous Motors

Synchronous motors run at a constant speed, exactly in step with the supply frequency, compared with the above types, which are asynchronous motors, as they do not run at the speed of synchronism. Their domestic application is to electric clocks which operate on the 50-cycle A.C. supply. One type require the spindle to be given a twist to start. The Warren clock motor makes use of the shaded-pole principle and is self-starting; the special shape of the rotor ensures that it runs at synchronous speed. The synchronous speed depends upon the number of magnet poles on the motor and not on the voltage. Synchronous motors run at this exact speed, whilst induction motors run some 5 to 7 per cent. slower. Series motors and various A.C. commutator motors run at speeds above and below synchronism. Table XV below gives the synchronous speed for various numbers of poles on a 50-cycle A.C. supply.

TABLE XV

Synchronous Motor Speeds on 50 Cyc./sec.

No. of Poles	2	4	6	8	10	12	16	20	24	30	40
Revs. per min.	3000	1500	1000	750	600	500	375	300	250	200	150

Vacuum Cleaners

The working parts of a vacuum cleaner consist of a high-speed motor with a shaft extension at one end to which is attached a fan. The motor is of the Universal type already described and may run at 10,000 revs. per min. From the table above it will be seen that the maximum speed for a synchronous or induction motor with two poles (one N. and one S.) is 3000 r.p.m. on 50 cyc./sec.

There are two types of vacuum cleaner, according to the arrangement of the dust-bag. In one the dust-bag is attached to the handle and the dust passes through the fan; in the other the dust-bag is of a special fabric inside a canister which allows the pressure due to the fan to suck the dust into the bag, the air being discharged over the motor or used at that end for " blowing " instead of " suction." The most frequent trouble is with the trailing flexible lead, which should be of good quality and must be frequently inspected for abrasion or cracks in the insulation. The motor brushes require periodical renewal; and if the motor will not start, a test should be taken to see if there is continuity of the series circuit.

Electric Washer

Various models are on the market and are of cabinet construction of welded sheet steel with a stove-enamel finish. The model illustrated in Fig. 144 is of the agitator type with a power-driven wringer and electric heater. A power-driven pump is provided which discharges the dirty water through a hose in a few minutes. This size of washer will take about 8 to 9 lb. of dry clothes. When not in use the wringer can be stored in a cupboard in the base of the machine and a stoved enamel table top is available if required. Overload protection is provided for the motor which is a $\frac{1}{4}$-h.p. single-phase induction motor only suitable for use on A.C. supplies, but various voltage ranges can be provided. The wringer is fitted with a safety pressure release mechanism so that if any article jams in the rollers (including fingers) immediate release is possible. The wringer can be turned to eight radial positions and is located by a spring catch. Should the heater be inadvertently left on so that the water boils away, or if there is no water in the tub, an automatic cut-out will switch off the heater. A 3-core tough rubber-covered cable is provided and the machine *must* be properly earthed. To obtain trouble-free service over many years and to maintain the washing machine in good condition it should be regularly inspected by an authorised dealer at least once a year, besides carrying out the simple maintenance specified.

An additional item is a rotary ironer which can be fitted interchangeably with the wringer. This is provided with a 26-in. long padded roller, rotated by the washing machine motor and has an electrically heated pressure shoe of stainless steel. A separate addition to the home laundry is a tumbler clothes dryer. In an electrically warmed breeze the wash is safely tumbled damp dry for ironing or bone dry as required. The control mechanism switches the machine off at the desired condition of the articles.

Domestic Electrical Refrigeration

A refrigerator suitable for domestic use must be effectively heat-insulated ; the door must be tight-fitting, so that there is no air leakage ; the internal air circulation must allow the warm air to flow easily over the cooling surfaces. Easy cleaning is essential, and the parts containing the

Approximate Weight of Dry Clothes

Pillow case	4 oz.	Hand towel	7 oz.	Cotton pyjamas	14 oz.
Child's dress	4 oz.	Man's shirt	8 oz.	Bath towel	1 lb.
Boy's shirt	6 oz.	Overall	9 oz.	Single sheet	1½ lb.
Man's cotton vest	6 oz.	Tablecloth	12 oz.	Double sheet	2½ lb.

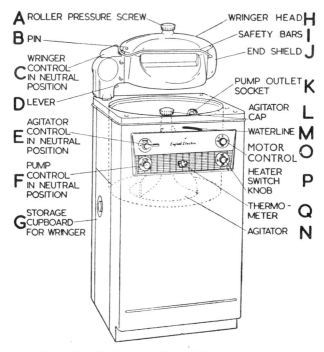

FIG. 144.—Cabinet Type Heater Washing Machine.
(*English Electric Co. Ltd.*)

I

refrigerant must be of robust construction so that there is no possibility of the escape of gases.

The electrical refrigerator can be either (a) mechanical or compression system, or (b) non-mechanical or absorption system.

In the former a motor-driven compressor is used, which is the more common arrangement.

Absorption refrigerators have been made for operation by electricity, gas, and oil. The inherent efficiency is much lower than the compression system; this method is now practically confined to gas operation.

Principle of Operation

When a liquid is vaporised, heat is required (i) to raise its temperature to boiling-point, called the sensible heat ; (ii) to convert the liquid to gas at the same temperature, called the latent heat.

If the liquid is kept in a vessel at some higher pressure, the boiling-point is raised; if this high-pressure liquid is allowed to pass into a vacuum or a much lower pressure, it immediately turns into gas, but at the same time heat is abstracted from its surroundings.

Refrigerants Used

The same principle applies to both types of refrigerators, but in the compression type sulphur dioxide, methyl chloride, and freon are used, whilst the absorption type uses ammonia as the refrigerant with hydrogen as the inert gas in the evaporator. In either method the evaporator is maintained some 20° F. below that of the refrigerator, thus heat passes from the air and food in the cabinet to the evaporator coils, causing any liquid refrigerant in the tubes to change to gas.

Operation of Compression Refrigeration

A simple diagram is given in Fig. 145 in which the evaporator coil is inside the cabinet, whilst the condenser coils are outside, generally below, adjacent to the motor-driven compressor. The evaporator coil is around the ice-making trays at the top, and the cold air falls to the lower spaces and is replaced by warm air from which the heat is abstracted. A single-cylinder single-acting compressor is shown; the suction-valve opens slightly before the piston reaches the

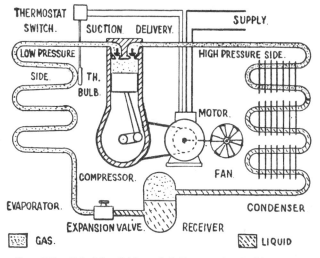

FIG. 145.—Principle of Air-cooled Compression Refrigerator.

bottom of its stroke, and gas enters the cylinder. When the piston begins to rise, both valves close and the gas is compressed ; at a certain pressure the delivery-valve opens and the high-pressure gas passes to the condenser. A slight loss of heat liquefies the gas, the cooling process being assisted by cool air from the fan blowing across the cooling-fins. The final cooling is carried out at the bottom of the condenser, which contains high-pressure liquid. The compressor cylinder is kept free of liquid and only deals with the gas. The gas volume is very much greater than an equal weight of liquid, so a high-pressure receiver is included in the circuit to contain the liquid, above which is some high-pressure gas. The receiver is connected to an expansion valve which allows some liquid to pass to the evaporator, with loss of pressure and absorption of heat, thus changing into gas. The cycle of operation is then repeated.

Temperature Control

A spirit-filled thermostat controls the interior temperature within an adjustable range. The thermostat bulb is against the evaporator and a capillary tube goes to the flexible copper bellows which operates the thermostat switch to start and stop the motor. The capacity of the plant, if running continuously, is several times that required to produce the necessary refrigeration, so the motor is automatically on intermittent duty. With the absorption type the refrigeration is more nearly continuous and there is not the same reserve of power.

The Motor

With frequent starting and stopping robust mechanical construction is essential, besides ample starting-torque for the compressor. The repulsion-start induction-run motor was originally used on A.C. supplies, but the capacitor motor is now used to a greater extent as it gives good starting-torque, is silent in operation, and free from radio interference. For D.C. supplies a compound motor is employed. For domestic refrigerators the motor output is from one-sixth horse-power, which is increased for larger cabinets, as the internal capacity goes from 3 to 20 cubic feet. For the larger sizes water-cooling is used, which may entail an extra charge in addition to that for electrical energy. Small models use about 350 units, whilst the 6-cubic-feet size consume about 500 units, per annum. The electric refrigerator is an example of precision engineering, and in the event of failure, which is most unlikely, expert attention should be obtained.

Power-factor has been referred to in connection with A.C. motors. With D.C. machines, true power in watts is given by the product of volts and amperes, but this is not always the case in A.C. circuits, in which this product is more often **volt-amperes**, which is only apparent power. With a lighting and heating load, which consists of a number of resistances, this product is watts, but with other apparatus, such as induction motors and transformers, more current is supplied than the true power appears to warrant. This condition brings in **power-factor**, which is the ratio

$$\frac{\text{True power}}{\text{Apparent power}} \quad \text{or} \quad \frac{\text{Watts}}{\text{Volt-amperes}}$$

With a resistance load the power-factor is unity, or it may be expressed as 100 per cent. ; but with inductive apparatus it is less than one, or below 100 per cent. Low power-factor means that more current is required for a given horse-power and adversely affects the supply system, so is often penalised in tariffs.

Current required by Motors

The output at the motor shaft-end is given in horse-power, and 1 h.p. = 746 watts, true power. Due to the motor losses, the watts input at the motor terminals must be greater than the output.

$$\text{For any sort of machine, Efficiency} = \frac{\text{Work got out}}{\text{Work put in}}$$

$$\text{For a D.C. motor, Efficiency} = \frac{746 \times \text{h.p. output}}{\text{Volts} \times \text{current input}}$$

$$\text{or Current input, in amperes} = \frac{746 \times \text{h.p.}}{\text{Volts} \times \text{efficiency}}$$

For small D.C. motors the efficiency is about 75 per cent., so the current required from the supply is given by :

$$\frac{746 \times \text{h.p.} \times 100}{\text{Volts} \times 75},$$

or as a first approximation by :

$$\text{D.C. motor current in amperes} = \frac{\text{h.p.} \times 1000}{\text{Volts}}.$$

The motor horse-power is given on the name-plate, together with the voltage on which it should be used.

With A.C. motors, besides the losses which affect the efficiency, there is power-factor, which still further increases the input current. With small motors the power-factor varies from under 70 to over 80 per cent. As the current is increased, power-factor goes in the denominator with efficiency. Hence for an A.C. motor :

Current input, in amperes

$$= \frac{746 \times \text{h.p. output}}{\text{Volts} \times \text{efficiency} \times \text{power-factor}}.$$

Fig. 146.—Portable Combined Ammeter and Voltmeter.
(*Nalder Bros. & Thompson Ltd.*)

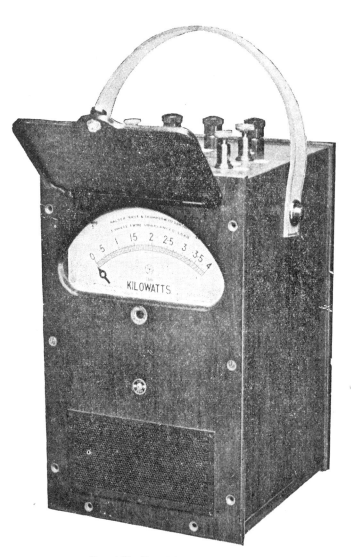

FIG. 147.—Portable Wattmeter.

(*Nalder Bros. & Thompson Ltd.*)

187

Taking an average value of 75 per cent. for both efficiency and power-factor, the current taken from the supply is given by :

$$\frac{746 \times \text{h.p.} \times 100 \times 100}{\text{Volts} \times 75 \times 75}$$

or A.C. motor current in amperes $= \dfrac{\text{h.p.} \times 1000 \times 4}{\text{Volts} \times 3}.$

Instruments for Power and Power-factor

On D.C. systems the product of voltage and current gives power in watts, which can be measured by a wattmeter, but an ammeter and voltmeter can be used to serve the same purpose. A portable combined ammeter and voltmeter is illustrated in Fig. 146. These instruments have

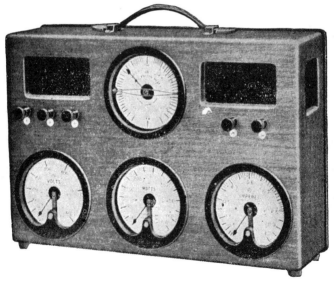

Fig. 148.—Portable A.C. Testing Set.

(Nalder Bros. & Thompson Ltd.)

several different ranges, with the respective terminals on the top of the case.

With A.C. supplies a wattmeter with terminals for both voltage and current is used, and Fig. 147 illustrates a portable wattmeter suitable for a 3-phase 4-wire A.C. system, which reads up to 4 kW.

Fig. 148 illustrates another portable testing set for A.C. measurements, and includes a voltmeter, wattmeter, ammeter, and power-factor meter. The author is indebted to Messrs. Nalder Bros. & Thompson Ltd. for these illustrations.

CHAPTER X

ACCUMULATORS

The Leclanché and other types of primary cells transform chemical energy into electrical energy, but are only suitable for small currents and intermittent use. For continuous duty and heavier currents secondary cells or accumulators are used. An accumulator has plates of certain chemical composition which are changed by the action of the charging current which passes from the positive plate to the negative plate through the electrolyte. When charging is complete, the reverse action is possible, the accumulator supplies a current and the plates revert to their original condition. These processes can be repeated without renewing the constituents of the cell, as is done with a primary battery.

There are two types of accumulator :

(i) The lead-acid cell, with lead plates treated with certain oxides in a solution (electrolyte) of dilute sulphuric acid.

(ii) The nickel-alkali cell, which has nickel-iron or nickel-cadmium plates with an electrolyte of concentrated potassium hydroxide.

Lead-acid Cell

The lead-acid cell is made up of pasted plates, the positive being red lead and the negative litharge, mixed with sulphuric acid. An initial forming process changes these plates to chocolate-coloured lead peroxide and spongy lead of a grey metallic colour. The brightness of these colours is one of the indications that such a battery is well charged and in good condition. When the terminals are connected to an external load, chemical changes occur, the plates go dull and the density of the electrolyte gets less, due to the formation of water. The density of the dilute sulphuric acid varies with the type of cell, around 1·21, and a measurement of the density with a hydrometer, illustrated in Fig. 149, is a good guide to the amount of charge left in the battery. Some wireless accumulators have a floating device which shows the state of charge, whilst large storage batteries installed in power-stations have hydrometers which float in the acid.

The electromotive force (e.m.f.) of a freshly charged battery is about 2·2 volts, when it is not supplying current ; but when load is applied the potential difference (p.d.) quickly falls to 2 volts, where it remains for some time, then gradually falls to 1·85 volts. A lead-acid cell should never be discharged below 1·8 volts or insoluble lead sulphate is formed on the plates. This is evident by white patches on the plates, which in time will ruin the battery.

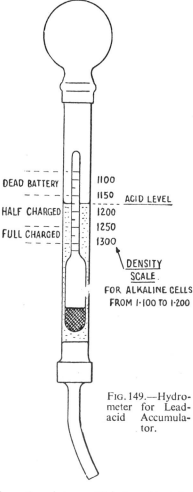

DEAD BATTERY

HALF CHARGED

FULL CHARGED

1100
1150   ACID LEVEL
1200
1250
1300

DENSITY SCALE.
FOR ALKALINE CELLS
FROM 1·100 TO 1·200

FIG. 149.—Hydrometer for Lead-acid Accumulator.

Care of Lead-acid Accumulator

The following points, if observed, will prolong the life of a battery :

1. Never leave the battery in a discharged state.   Charge the battery if the density falls below the minimum stated on the label (about 1·150).

2. A voltmeter reading across the terminals, without any load, is deceptive ; it may be 2 V., but when load is taken fall below 1·8 V.

3. Keep to the recommended charge and discharge rates specified by the maker.

4. The level of the electrolyte must be kept above the top of the plates by adding distilled water.   Concentrated sulphuric acid should not be added.   In mixing the electrolyte the acid should always be added to the water ; the other way round is disastrous.

5. All connections should be kept clean and well smeared with vaseline.

6. Do not short-circuit the battery with a piece of wire; you may burn your fingers, and in any case it will loosen the paste and may buckle the plates.

Nickel-alkaline Cell

The positive plate in each case is nickelic hydroxide held in a grid of nickel, whilst the negative plate is a special mixture of iron oxide or cadmium carried in nickelled-steel plates.   The electrolyte is potassium hydroxide (caustic potash), which is a corrosive liquid with a specific gravity about 1·18.   The electrolyte does not change in density, so only very occasional make-up with a little distilled water is needed.

The average voltage of an alkaline cell is 1·2 V., so more are required to make up a given battery voltage than the lead cell with a p.d. of 2 V.   The advantages of this cell are its light weight, ability to withstand mechanical abuse, freedom from " sulphating," can be overcharged and over-discharged and left uncharged for long periods. The disadvantages are higher first cost and more cells are required to make up a given voltage.

Capacity of a Battery

This is given on the label in ampere-hours at the 10-hour rate, e.g. a 40-amp.-hour battery means that it will supply 4 amperes for 10 hours, if in good condition. With higher discharge rates the same capacity is not possible. With a

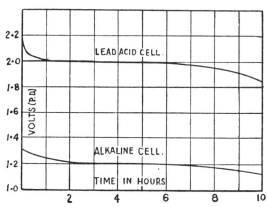

FIG. 150.—Discharge Characteristics of Lead-acid and Alkaline Cells.

lead cell, if the current is increased 50 per cent. to 6 amp., it will only last 60 per cent., i.e. 6 hours, before the p.d. falls to 1·8 volts. With currents below 4 amp. the ampere-hours obtained are somewhat above the rated capacity. The number of ampere-hours on discharge to that required to recharge the cell (amp.-hour efficiency) is about 90 per cent. for a lead cell and 75–80 per cent. for an alkaline cell, though the latter has less difference of capacity with discharge current. Comparative characteristic curves are given in Fig. 150.

Methods of Charging Accumulators

Accumulators can be charged from D.C. supplies by inserting a resistance in series to " drop " the difference of voltage, at the required charging current.   But this method is wasteful, as this example will show.

Example 17. A 12-volt car-battery is charged at 15 volts 5 amp. from a 110-V. D.C. supply.   What resistance must be connected in series ?   What will be the loss in the resistance and the cost of charging for 24 hours, assuming the mean charging current is 4 amp., and electricity cost 1d. per unit ?

Volts drop in resistance $= 110 - 15 = 95$ volts.

Value of resistance $= \frac{95}{5} = 19$ ohms, to carry 5 amp.

Loss in resistance $(I^2R) = 5^2 \times 19 = 472 \cdot 5$ watts

(compared with $15 \times 5 = 75$ watts input to battery).

$$\text{Cost per 24 hours} = \frac{110 \times 4 \times 24}{1000} \times 1d. = 10 \cdot 6d$$

Another method is to use a motor-generator set, consisting of either an A.C. or D.C. motor driving a low-voltage generator suited to the batteries to be charged.   This method is carried out either by the constant-current method, in which batteries with similar charging currents are grouped together in series and the generator voltage is adjusted to keep the current constant ;   or the constant-potential method, in which batteries of similar voltages are connected in parallel across bus-bars, the charging current being large to begin with and gradually tapering off. These methods are only suitable for many batteries where skilled attention is available.   When the lead-acid cell is fully charged it " gases," and naked lights or sparking connections or contacts must not be allowed near the battery, as the hydrogen evolved forms an explosive mixture with air.

The car-battery in service is charged by a special type of generator driven off the engine, and the circuit includes a

" cut-out " which completes the charging circuit when the voltage of the dynamo is high enough to provide a charging current.

Private generating sets in large establishments generally contain a battery large enough to supply the lights for some time, though the floating-battery type with a small battery and automatic action is now very popular. These plants are beyond the scope of this book and the automatic type is generally too complicated for the amateur to attempt to rectify any faults.

For the small wireless accumulator and car-battery, static types of chargers are most suitable. These may be of the

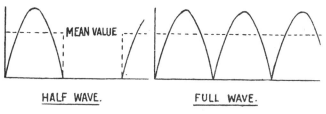

HALF WAVE.   FULL WAVE.

FIG. 151.—Illustrating Rectification.

valve rectifier type or the dry-plate rectifier type. Alternating current is not suitable for charging batteries so it has to be " rectified "—that is, only the positive half of the wave is fed to the battery, or by another arrangement the negative half is brought over to the positive side, as indicated in Fig. 151. This unidirectional current is quite satisfactory as the equipment consists of a transformer to reduce the A.C. voltage, which is then passed to the rectifier. A fuse must be fitted and it is also necessary to include a resistance on the output side, so that if the rectifier is short-circuited the current is limited to the safe value.

Car-battery Trickle Chargers

These chargers are dry-plate rectifiers with plug connection on the high-voltage side for a range of A.C. voltages from 200 to 250.   On the output side connections can be made suitable for 2-, 6-, and 12-volt batteries.   The charger is supplied with a length of cable and plug to fit in a special socket on the dash-board.   The plug can only be put in one way, so that the correct polarity is ensured.

GARAGE EQUIPMENT

All garage socket-outlets should be of the iron-clad type mounted about 4 feet 6 inches up the wall, with earthing connections if used for small portable tools such as drills and grinders.   Portable hand-lamps should be of the " all-insulated type," in which it is impossible to touch any metal part of the lamp-cap.   For certain uses, low-voltage

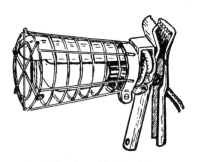

FIG. 152.—Portable Hand-lamp.

lighting is preferable, e.g. air-raid shelters, in which low-power lighting is obtained from batteries or a double-wound transformer which steps the voltage down from 230 to 12 volts.   A portable hand-lamp is illustrated in Fig. 152, with a strong wire guard, but another pattern has one of moulded material.   The gripping attachment is useful as it leaves both hands free for the job.   Flimsy flexible should not be used ; either T.R.S. or a good-quality workshop flex should be fitted and examined periodically to see that it is in good order.

ELECTRIC SHOCK—RESCUE AND TREATMENT

This section is taken from *Electric Shock—Its Effects and Treatment*, by Gilbert Burnet, M.C., M.B., Ch.B., M.I.Fire E., Hon. Chief Surgeon National Fire Brigades Association, and included by kind permission of that author and the *Electrical Times*, in which the full article was published in 1938.

Rescue

The method of rescue of a victim from a live circuit is almost too well known to require repetition. At the same time, I feel compelled to repeat that all insulating material used by the rescuer must be *dry*. Moreover, at the risk of appearing childish, I must continue to teach that it may be quicker to break the circuit by a switch. Recently, I experienced a safe rescue, by a well-trained man, who used a rope, and dropped a dry packing-case lid on which to stand. I congratulated him on the quick rescue, but was able to convince him that the main switch was as near to him as the packing-case. There is no doubt that, in my opinion, of all emergencies calling for " first aid," that of electric shock requires more cool and collected thought than any other.

General Treatment

It has been pointed out that the most dominant symptom of severe electric shock is arrested respiration, and its resultant asphyxia. Respiratory movements must be carried on *at once*, not only because of a possible stoppage of a feebly working heart, but because of the damage done by asphyxia. Lack of oxygen, supplied to the blood by the lungs, means loss of vitality to all living cells ; stagnation of these cells may mean death to them, and a subsequent small hæmorrhage in their place—especially in the brain.

The longer the asphyxia, the greater the damage, and the less likelihood of a successful resuscitation. In other words, as soon as the circuit is broken artificial respiration must be carried on at once, and continued until the victim is resuscitated. It must be continued during the dressing of any sort of injury, and even during a doctor's examination ; the victim must not be allowed to miss one single breath.

Local Treatment

In simple burns of the first degree, in which pain may be a prominent feature, local treatment may well be on the same lines as that for ordinary burns. Lint, wetted with a 1 per cent. solution of picric acid, will, if applied early, relieve pain and prevent blistering. Tannic-acid preparations also may serve a useful purpose.

In severe electric shock, however, the burns by electricity differ from ordinary burns, in causing a greater destruction of the tissues. In this type of case, wet dressings and tannic acid should *not* be used ; not only because they may not agree with the subsequent treatment which is sure to be required, but also because of the risk of delayed hæmorrhage, as well as sepsis. The majority of these cases will be best treated by the application of a dry sterile dressing or an antiseptic gauze of the cyanide or picric type.

Artificial Respiration

In spite of all difference of opinion here and on the Continent, in face of all the mechanical devices for carrying out a man's respiratory movements, there is at present only one method of artificial respiration which can be carried out successfully, unaided, immediately, and single-handed, and that is Schäfer's. It is the duty of every man who has to deal with electricity to learn how to carry out this method of keeping a man's breathing going, and I make no excuse for giving this method in detail as follows :

(*a*) Quickly turn the victim flat on his stomach, face downwards, head to one side (or, if preferred, the head resting on one forearm), with arms lying at each side of the head.

(*b*) Facing his head, kneel astride his buttocks and allow your body weight to be taken by your heels.

(*c*) Place your flat hands with closed fingers over and well round the victim's loins just above his hips. Keep your thumbs directed towards his head, and almost parallel to, but a short distance from, his spine.

(*d*) Lean forward on to your straight arms, so that your body weight exerts a steady but increasing pressure on the patient's loins. This presses the abdomen, with its contents, against the ground, and thus drives air out of his lungs. During this pressure, count " twenty-one ; twenty-two ; twenty-three ; twenty-four." During the word " four," which is slightly prolonged, relaxation of pressure is made by swinging the body weight back to the heels. Air is thus sucked into the lungs by the elasticity of the chest. Counting in this manner will ensure the necessary rhythmical movements of 15 per minute.

Not a single movement must be omitted until the victim has been resuscitated (that is, until he has recovered normal breathing) or until an expert has taken the responsibility of certifying that his heart has definitely stopped and that he is dead. It is of great importance that he should be resuscitated as soon as possible. Artificial respiration will keep him alive, but often other means are required to resuscitate him.

Resuscitation

Artificial respiration and " resuscitation " are by no means synonymous. In some text-books they are represented as such, perhaps on account of the frequent successes of Schäfer's method. Artificial respiration merely carries on a suspended normal respiration, while resuscitation means a revival of normal spontaneous breathing. In other words, a passive resuscitation may be brought about by continuing the acts of breathing, but a recovery to normal may be accelerated by the use of some active means of stimulating the depressed functions.

In electrical accidents it is especially important to employ as soon as possible some means of re-establishing the normal function of the respiratory centre, which is so commonly the prime factor. Many drugs have been suggested and tried, but the results have not been encouraging.

It has been proved beyond doubt that oxygen will not stimulate the respiratory centres ; in my opinion, it only prolongs the artificial respiration, although it certainly will relieve the asphyxia. Carbon-dioxide is the normal stimulant in the blood of the respiratory centre ; and when resuscitation is required, carbon-dioxide will succeed, if anything will. If this is used in a non-poisonous atmosphere there is no need for any extra oxygen with the attendant cumbersome cylinders which the use of this gas entails.

Easily compressed carbon-dioxide may be contained in cylinders small enough to be carried in the waistcoat pocket. Advantage has been taken of this fact by the manufacturers, who have introduced various types of apparatus for its convenient use. The simplest apparatus consist of a metal holder, capable of piercing a gas-bulb, from which the gas may be collected into a rubber bag and delivered through a face-piece, and mixed in the desired concentration with the inspired air. In the absence of a bag and face-piece, the gas may be sprayed directly around the face of the victim during the carrying out of Schäfer's method of artificial respiration.

Conclusion

There is no doubt that the best treatment in all cases of severe electric shock is Schäfer's method of artificial respiration *at once* and continued with carbon-dioxide as a resuscitation agent as soon as it can possibly be procured. By this means the period of asphyxia will be reduced to a minimum, cell damage avoided, and a successful revival secured.

INDEX